CW00751213

The History of Lead Mining
in the North East of England

by

Les Turnbull

ERGO
PRESS
Publishing for Northumberland

THE HISTORY OF LEAD MINING
IN THE NORTH EAST OF ENGLAND

First published 1975 by H. Hill and Son
Second revised edition © L.Turnbull 1985
Published 1987 by Sandhill Press, Alnwick
Third revised edition published by ERGO PRESS
© Les Turnbull 2006

Fourth revised edition published by ERGO PRESS
© Les Turnbull 2008

ISBN: 978-0-9552758-2-1

ERGO
PRESS
5, St Mary's Chare
Hexham
Northumberland
NE46 1NQ
Tel: 01434 689653

ergo.press@yahoo.co.uk
www.ergopress.com

Written, published and printed in Northumberland

Acknowledgements

The original publication of this book was made possible by the generous assistance of many individuals and institutions. I am particularly indebted to Gateshead Education Committee for their encouragement and especially to John McMillan, then Deputy Director, who first sparked off my interest in lead mining and to whom this book is dedicated. Professor Norman McCord and George Pearson of the University of Newcastle read the original manuscript and suggested several improvements. The staff of the North of England Mining Institute, Beamish Museum, Northumberland County Record Office, Cumbria County Record Office, Newcastle City Library and Newcastle University Library were very helpful with the research.

In this revised fourth edition I am grateful to Beamish Museum for permission to use the photographs on pages 4, 13, 18, 28, 29, 32, 53, 64, 66, 69, 74, 76 and 117. I am also grateful to Jack Young of Langley for permission to use the slides of Albert Gifford which illustrate life in the dales at the turn of the century on pages 12, 17, 20, 51, 52, 73, 77, 79, 82, 84, 91 and 92.

Finally, I wish to acknowledge the initiative of Julia and Alan Grint of Ergo Press in promoting both the third and fourth editions, and for their help in making the revisions.

Les Turnbull BA (Hons), MEd
Newcastle upon Tyne 2008

Chapter One

The Lead Dales of North East England

The northern Pennine orefield is a barren expanse of moorland bounded in the south by the Stainmore Pass, in the west by the Cross Fell escarpment, in the north by the Tyne Gap and in the east by the Durham coalfield. Most of this wild but beautiful plateau lies between one thousand and two thousand feet above sea level and the former mining communities within its dales are amongst the highest and most isolated settlements in the country. The basic reason for the colonisation of this inhospitable land was the presence of rich deposits of argentiferous galena – a silver-bearing lead ore – which is why the upper valleys of the rivers Tees, Wear, Derwent, Allen and the South Tyne are known as 'the lead dales'. However, it would be wrong to infer that lead mining was the only activity in the dales: farming, quarrying and the mining of other minerals were all practised in the past. Today the principal sources of employment are farming and the burgeoning tourist industry.

Within the lead dales the surface rocks belong mainly to the carboniferous limestone group consisting of a succession of limestones, shales, thin coal seams and sandstones. In places, especially in the south and east, the Millstone Grit caps the high ground which is purple with heather in summertime. More important economically are the outcrops of the Great and Little Limestones which form the distinctive scars of the valley sides. Another notable feature is the intrusion of the Whin Sill which outcrops principally in Teesdale where it has caused the spectacular waterfalls at Cauldron Snout and High Force. These surface rocks are cut by vertical mineral veins which generally run in a north-easterly or a north-westerly direction. The veins contain a mixture of minerals – the most common being quartz, calcite, fluorspare, witherite, barites, spathose

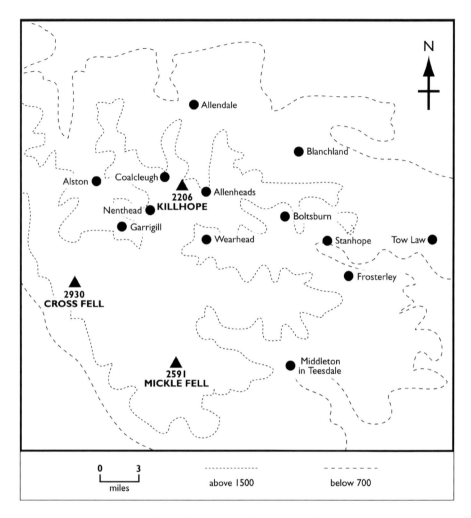

iron ore and zinc blende – which were known to the lead miner as *gangue* or waste material.

The *oreshoots* of lead ore are found in these veins but they are generally only wageable – or worth mining – in the limestone beds and especially in the Great Limestone. Most of the lead veins are argentiferous, the silver content amounting to less than ten ounces in the ton of lead. The oreshoots of argentiferous galena are vertical and vary in size from a few inches to twenty feet or more. Sometimes there are horizontal oreshoots known as *flats* which contain the richest ore. In his reports about the flats associated with the Coronation vein in the Allenheads mine the manager, William Crawhall, wrote about "solid lumps of pure ore upward of one hundredweight" and "cavities after cavities full or ore". Flats are usually found in the Great Limestone.

The scattered cottages and the patchwork of enclosed fields are a reminder that the dales were first farmed as an adjunct of mining: the miner's cottage was architecturally a farmstead, with a barn, hayloft and living quarters all under one roof. The cultivation of grass and the rearing of sheep and cattle are now the sole farming activities in the dales. Surprisingly, *arable* farming was practised during the lead mining era, which is unusual at heights above seven hundred feet. These smallholdings were an important additional source of income to the miners and in the nineteenth century they also provided employment for the womenfolk who were not given employment in the mining industry. The numerous lime-kilns are a reminder of the importance of the lime burning industry in the battle to win fields from the moorland waste. As a consequence of the collapse of the mining industry in the late nineteenth century, the dales became depopulated. Many of the farm buildings were abandoned to decay and the smallholdings were amalgamated to form larger farms. Some of the outfields reverted to moorland. Today, many of the buildings have been restored and are used as weekend homes or holiday cottages which provide extra income for the local farmers.

Quarrying

Quarrying developed initially to supply the needs of the locality for sandstone, used to build farmsteads, cottages and field walls, and for limestone, used as a fertilizer and a cement. With the demand for fertilizer growing as a result of the agricultural improvements of the early nineteenth century and, more importantly, the development of the iron and steel industry in the mid-nineteenth century, the demand for limestone so increased that large scale exploitation of the Great and Little Limestones took place, especially in Weardale. Stanhope became a centre of lime burning and iron smelting and was linked to both Tyneside and Teesside by rail. Ganister, a sandstone with a high silica content which is also used in the iron and steel industry, was quarried from the Millstone Grit. With the decline of the lead industry in the late nineteenth century, quarrying became increasingly important and, besides limestone and ganister, whinstone was quarried for road building. At Frosterley the marble quarries became famous – examples of this polished limestone can be seen in the parish church at Stanhope.

Ruins of the Iron Furnace at Stanhopeburn

4

Iron Mining

Spathose iron ore, or '*rider* ore' as the lead miners called it because it was found in the mineral veins and flats of the lead mines, is an iron carbonate with about 40% metal content which has been mined chiefly in Weardale but also at Nenthead and Alston. Records of iron ore mining in Weardale date back to the twelfth century, but it was not until the formation of the Weardale Iron Company in 1842 by Charles Attwood, a Gateshead factory owner who was prominent in the Chartist movement, that iron ore was mined on a large scale. By the late 1850s, the company's railway system had reached the Slitt Pasture ironstone mines and 1,700 men were employed by the company in Weardale. At first the ore was smelted at Stanhope but in 1845 furnaces were built at Tow Law and Tudhoe on the edge of the coalfield. In 1862, steel manufacture began at Wolsingham. The Weardale Iron Company had become the largest firm mining iron in the northern Pennines and in the 1870s over 100,000 tons of ore were extracted each year. However, by the 1880s the great age was over and by the end of the century iron ore mining had practically ceased in the dales, although Tudhoe continued to be supplied by iron from Carricks Level and Rookhope until 1905.

Zinc

Although calamine and blende, the carbonate and sulphide of zinc, are found in the lead veins of Allendale and Nentdale, they had no commercial value until the nineteenth century because zinc (frequently known as spelter) could be supplied more cheaply by Germany. A few local ventures are recorded such as that of Richard Grey who redressed the old spoil heaps at the Nenthead Fields mine and the Haggs mine between 1794 and about 1831. In 1817, Thomas Shaw and Company leased part of the Langley mill to smelt the large quantities of blende which were being raised from their mines at Guddamgill and Brownley Hill in the Nent valley. The zinc furnace at Langley employed six men in 1822 but the venture was abandoned soon afterwards as a result of the price of zinc falling from £30 to £10 per ton. In 1845 a spelter works was built by James Henry Attwood at Tindale, a coal mining village some twenty miles north-west of Nenthead, which smelted the annual produce from the Cumberland mines for the next fifty years.

Besides being needed to make brass (an alloy of copper and zinc) zinc was also used to galvanise iron; it may be no accident that this development coincided with the expansion of the Attwood family's interests in iron manufacture. The output of zinc was only a few hundred tons in the 1840s but when, in 1883, the Nenthead and Tynedale and Zinc Company took over the leases of the Nenthead mines from the London Lead Company, the mining of zinc became more important than that of lead. Whilst the price of lead continued to fall in the late nineteenth century, the price of zinc steadily increased and therefore the Nenthead company developed production until it reached a peak of 5,550 tons in 1895.

Unfortunately for this local enterprise, the lease for the zinc works at Tindale expired in that year and because it was unable to secure favourable terms the company sold its mining interests to Vieille Montagne Zinc. This Belgian firm was the largest manufacturer of zinc products in the world and in subsequent years it extended its mining leases to include mines in the West Allen valley and elsewhere in Nentdale. In 1899 the company leased Coalcleugh mine and by 1918 had raised 50,000 tons. A new dressing plant was built at Nenthead in 1909 but unfortunately for the local economy all of the zinc was smelted abroad.

Fluorspar

Other waste products of the lead mining era – witherite, barites and fluorspar – acquired a commercial value as a result of the demands of industry in the late nineteenth century. By far the most important was the demand for fluorspar by the iron and steel industry. The introduction of the basic open-hearth method of manufacturing steel resulted in the large scale mining of fluorspar which in the northern orefield was developed by the Weardale Iron Company and the Weardale Lead Company. Although fluorspar is principally used as a flux in the steel industry, it is also the chief source of fluorine compounds which are widely used in the making of plastics, heat resistant enamels and fluorine anaesthetics. Before the Second World War most of the fluorspar was collected by redressing the spoil heaps of old lead mines but later the mines themselves were opened for spar. At Allenheads, British Steel operated the mine between 1969 and 1979; Whiteheaps mine in the Derwent Valley was worked intermittently for fluorspar between 1921 and 1980 by several companies including British Steel. Groverake in Weardale was operated by British Steel until 1985

Lead Mining – A Brief History

The lead industry was more important than any of the industries already mentioned. The development of the lead industry not only resulted in the colonisation of the dales and the establishment of mining communities but it also made the region famous in the eighteenth and nineteenth centuries as the principal lead mining area of Britain, at a time when Britain was the world's largest producer of lead. This industry ranks first in the history of the dales by any assessment, be it the value of the products, the volume of ore extracted or the number of men employed; it was also the only industry to be fully established in the dales with dressing plants and smelting works as well as mines.

Unlike ironstone mining and limestone quarrying, and also the twentieth century ventures for zinc and fluorspar, the lead industry was not simply an extractive industry using the raw materials of the area to promote industrial activity elsewhere. It created, in an otherwise barren and desolated region, a society with a distinctive character, the history of which provides a refreshing contrast to the history of the great northern coalfield. There were no great disasters to compare with the accidents at Felling (1812), Hartley (1862), or Seaham (1880); there was an absence of class conflict such as typified the strikes of 1832 and 1844 and indeed the general history of trade unionism amongst the coalminers. Through the provision of schools, housing, libraries and medical services the lead mining companies provided an example to their counterparts in the coalfield and earned the support of a willing labour force without destroying the independence and freedom which the lead miners prized most.

As a result of foreign competition, chiefly from Spain, the lead industry collapsed at the end of the nineteenth century and this society suffered a death blow. However, because of their isolated position, many of the physical remains of the industry survive to be explored by those who have the energy and enthusiasm to roam the northern dales.

The *origins* of lead mining in the northern dales are obscure, but in view of the readiness with which the Romans exploited the mineral resources of the Mendips, Wales, Derbyshire and Yorkshire, it seems probable that this northern area was first worked immediately after the subjection of the Brigantes by Agricola, *circa* AD 79. The road from Kirkby Thore to Carvoran – The Maiden Way – runs through the Alston Moor mining district and lead seals naming the Second Cohort of Nervians, which was stationed at Whitley Castle, a Roman Fort near Alston, have been found at Brough under Stainmore.

The silver mines of Alston Moor were internationally famous at a later time, but whether Whitley Castle was the centre of Roman mining in the north and a heavily fortified bullion store can only be decided after further excavation. It is interesting that the lead found at Corbridge contained torbanite, a mineral allied to cannel coal which has been identified in some of the Alston Moor veins. Further, Sopwith, an eminent nineteenth century mining engineer, considered that The Chesters near Garrigill was a place where the Romans had mined lead. More significant is the fact that the later mines at Fallowfield, Stonecroft, Langley Barony and Settlingstones lie close to the early frontier on the Stanegate and to the later frontier formed by Hadrian's Wall.

During the Christian era, Britain, Spain and Sardinia replaced Greece as the principal source of lead for the Roman world but these areas were all abandoned with the decline of the Roman Empire in the west. However, in Germany the skills of mining, dressing and smelting lead ore were kept alive; with the revival of the industry in Europe during the Middle Ages, Germany became the centre of technical expertise. In the twelfth century, the great activity in castle and church building created an enormous demand for lead to be used for roofing and piping. The Derbyshire mines were then the most important in Britain but the mines of the northern dales were not idle. In the reign of Henry II, lead was sent from the Alston Moor mines not only to the king's palace at Windsor but also to the famous Cistercian abbey founded by St Bernard at Clairvaux. The first documentary evidence exists in the Pipe Roll of 1130-31 which records the payment of one hundred shillings for a silver mine to King Henry I, by the burgesses of Carlisle. This and later references to the Carlisle silver mines undoubtedly referred to the mines on Alston Moor which supplied the Carlisle mint. The Prince Bishops of the Palatinate of Durham were actively encouraging the development of mining in Weardale during the twelfth century and the Pipe Roll of 1196-97 has a reference to the purchase of lead for the mint at Durham.

The shortage of bullion in Europe during the fifteenth century was the second major impetus to the development of mining throughout Europe during medieval times – again, the technical and commercial skills of the Germans were in demand. Stimulated by royal protection and ecclesiastical patronage, the northern orefield shared in the general expansion of mining activities. The accounts of the Ecclesiastical Commissioners record work in 1426 upon the Sedling vein in Weardale and name mines in operation at Hardrake, Ireshope and Blakden, where John Westwood and partners were working at the Watergate (the adit). Smelting is mentioned at "les bolehills" at Wolsingham. Individual mines in the Derwent valley and on Alston Moor are named in the late fifteenth century.

In 1474 a commission was appointed to investigate the statement of George Willarby that "there are three notable mines in the north of England of which one contains 27lbs of silver in a fodder of lead with a vein a quarter rod in breadth". The report prompted King Edward IV to grant four mines to his brother Richard, to Henry Earl of Northumberland and to two merchants: *Shildon* (near Blanchland), *Fletcheras* (near Nenthead), *Richmond* and *Keswick*. The king also appointed Walter Barsonhousen, a German metallurgist, to be responsible for the smelting and refining of the ore.

The encouragement and protection given to foreigners by the Crown was important because the German skills in mining, dressing and smelting the ores were far in advance of their counterparts elsewhere in Europe. In 1528, Henry VIII appointed Joachim Hochsteter to be "the principal surveyor and master of all mines in England and Ireland"; indeed, throughout the sixteenth century there was an influx of German miners into Britain. These men would no doubt be familiar with the advanced techniques illustrated by Agricola in his masterly account of German mining practices, *De Re Metallica*, published in 1556. The mine at Blagill and the refining mill at

Blaydon could have been named by German workers, *blei* being German for lead.

In the late sixteenth century there were important technological developments, all of which are described in Agricola's book. There was a greater use of levels for entering and draining the mines, which was a popular method in Germany. Improved methods were now used to dress the ore and they proved so much more efficient in separating the galena from the waste material that poor people in Derbyshire were even able to make a living by re-dressing the spoil heaps of old workings. In 1565, William Humphay (sic) was granted letters patent for a more efficient method of smelting – the open hearth furnace – which had previously been illustrated by Agricola. Since the open hearth furnace used only *half* the fuel needed for the bolehill it was speedily adopted. Royal patronage – inspired by the need for money in a period of inflation – reached a climax in the reign of Elizabeth with the incorporation of the Mines Royal Company in 1568.

Despite the efforts of successive English sovereigns, the shortage of bullion remained, but they did succeed in developing the mining industry. All of the mining districts appear to have enjoyed growth in the sixteenth and seventeenth centuries with the notable exception of Alston Moor where the mines were considered to be exhausted in 1629. Matthew Bee of Ninebanks in Allendale, who opened mines at Grewslacke, Spartywell and Bates Hill in 1565, was typical of the many prospectors operating on a small scale who dominated the industry during this period. According to a survey of Stanhope Park dated 1595, Sir William Bowes owned a mill at Burtreeford which was used to smelt ore from his mines in Teesdale and Weardale. The building of this mill, together with recorded complaints of a shortage of timber in the Bishop's parks, is further evidence of expansion. In fact, it is clear from the Moor Masters' Account Books that most of the veins on the estates belonging to the Bishop of Durham were known by 1666.

Despite the Civil War, the lead industry continued to flourish and trade developed with the Continent, the Mediterranean and with the East Indies. Equally important was the repeal of the Mines Royal Act in 1693 which gave every landowner the right to develop and profit from the mineral resources on his estates. It is significant that the two great companies which were to dominate the industry for the next two centuries – the Blackett-Beaumont and the London Lead Company – were formed at this time.

The Gin Hill Shaft at Allenheads

The Blackett-Beaumont Company

The Blackett family had mined in Allendale since at least 1684; when Sir William Blackett bought the manor of Hexham from Sir John Fenwick in 1694 the foundations of the Blackett's lead mining empire had been laid. To these lands in Northumberland were added the mining grounds in Weardale which were leased from the Bishop of Durham in 1698. The Blacketts owned the great mines at Burtree Pasture in Weardale, at Coalcleugh in the West Allen valley, and at Allenheads in the East Allen valley. The smelt mills at Dukesfield, Catton, Rookhope and Dirt Pot and the refinery and warehouses at Blaydon also belonged to this powerful family.

Wolfcleugh Mine and Railway

Thomas Sopwith and other principal engineers of the Blackett-Beaumont company, were responsible for the extensive construction of levels for the drainage, for exploration and for the better management of the mines. Their initiative prompted the harnessing of the abundant local water supplies to drive the hydraulic machinery used in the mines, on the dressing floors and at the smelt mills which took place in the eighteenth and nineteenth centuries. Equally impressive were the welfare facilities provided by the Blackett-Beaumont family, most notably the provision of schools for the workmen and their families. The family worked the mines in the Allendales and Weardale until the industry collapsed two hundred years later; an event which is fittingly marked by the closure, in 1896, of Allenheads mine, once the largest silver-lead mine in the world. Although several years later the Beaumont Company opened the Sipton mine, the days of greatness had passed.

The London Lead Company – The 'Quaker Company'

The London Lead Company – also known as the Quaker Company – was formed by a grant of a royal charter in 1692 and in 1696 leases were taken out on the Blagill and Tynehead mines on Alston Moor. In the eighteenth century, this company acquired more leases on Alston Moor and extended its interests to include mines in the Derwent valley and in Teesdale. The Derwent mines were abandoned by the Quaker Company at the beginning of the nineteenth century, but afterwards they were worked by Easterby Hall and Company, and then by the Derwent Mining Company which built Hunstanworth as its capital.

However, the Alston Moor mines (centred upon Nenthead), and the Teesdale mines (with their centre at Middleton), experienced an industrial revolution. Like the Blacketts, the Quaker Company was able to finance the construction of long levels for drainage and exploration, to develop the use of hydraulic power and to promote education and other welfare schemes. The London Lead Company was also noted for the development of the *reverberatory furnace* which differed from the open hearth furnace in that the ore was separated from the fuel and it was therefore possible to use coal instead of charcoal, which by the eighteenth century was in very short supply. During the late nineteenth century, the dramatic fall in lead prices occurring at a time when capital was needed for exploration caused the company to abandon its mines on Alston Moor in 1883. The Teesdale mines continued in operation until 1905 when the London Lead Company finally wound up business.

No survey of lead mining in the northern Pennines would be complete without mentioning the Commissioners of Greenwich Hospital for Seamen, who were granted in 1734 much of the land formerly belonging to the Derwentwater family which had been confiscated because of the Earl's part in the Jacobite rebellion of 1715. The Commissioners leased the mineral rights on Alston Moor largely to the London Lead Company for a royalty which amounted to one-fifth of the ore produced. The ore was then normally resold to the company for smelting. However, in 1768 the Commissioners opened their own mill at Langley which was operated by the Greenwich Hospital until 1833; and then by a private company, Shield and Dinning, until it was finally dismantled in 1887. Pattison was assay master at Langley Mill before working for the Blackett-Beaumont Company at Blaydon, where he developed the crystallisation process for the separation of silver from lead in 1833. This was an event of international significance.

Mining was never exclusively the concern of the major companies since the lure of hidden riches continued to attract groups of prospectors. Unfortunately, very little is known of these small enterprises except for the few mentioned in reports, two of these being the Rotherhope Fell

Company and the legendary Hudgill Burn Company. The mine at Hudgill Burn in Nentdale became famous because two old mines, abandoned as unprofitable, were reopened and great wealth was quickly made. The company was formed in 1813 with £500 capital and during the seventeen years in which it was productive it made an astonishing £320,000 profit. It was every miner's dream, but it was also an exceptional case and – as with all gambling ventures – was later used to delude others.

The great development of the lead industry in England at the beginning of the eighteenth century coincided with the failure to revive the Spanish mines and the steady decline of the mines in Germany. Thus, by the middle of the century, Britain was the world's leading producer and the northern dales were the most important lead mining district in Britain. The lead industry benefited from the enormous expansion of British trade during the eighteenth century. Furthermore, its value as the most corrosive-resistant of the common metals, which had long been appreciated, became increasingly significant as the pace of technological development increased. Lead was needed for piping, building materials, for type and castings and as a base in the paint industry – to mention but a few of its commercial uses.

As a result of the successful lead trade a number of ancilliary industries also developed on Tyneside during the late eighteenth and early nineteenth centuries. The great warehouses and refinery of the Beaumont Company were beside Blaydon railway station and next to the white lead works of Dr Richardson. The owners of the Derwent mines had a large lead works at Bill Quay while the Blacketts had interests in the Tyne Lead Works at Hebburn and St Anthony's Lead Works at Newcastle. On the north side of the river, at Elswick, was the Patent Shot Works of Walker and Parker with its distinctive shot tower. This factory, together with Cookson's Chemical Works at Willington and at Howden became part of

Groverake Lead Mine in Rookhope
The spoil-heap belongs to the ironstone workings

Elswick Shot Tower

Associated Lead. Near Byker Bridge was the Ouseburn Lead Works which became part of British Paints.

In the nineteenth century, Britain's lead mining industry continued to expand but its dominance was challenged by foreign companies which had often been developed using British capital and expertise. In particular, English initiatives revived mining in Spain at the ancient centre of Linares and the neighbouring province of Murcia. This, together with developments in other provinces, resulted in Spain replacing Britain as the world's major source of lead. Although by the 1850s British exports had been greatly reduced, this loss was offset by an increase in home demand created by the continued expansion of industry and – more importantly – the spread of urbanisation regulated by new building legislation. Thus the British lead industry enjoyed a period of prosperity and expansion in the 1850s but its position amongst the world's lead-producing nations, and even its security at home, was being challenged by developments beyond its control.

Lead-mining in Germany was revived as a result of state and private enterprise and by the end of the century production had reached 100,000 tons. In the USA there was a four-fold increase in production during the late nineteenth century, largely as a result of the development of the Colorado and Idaho orefields.

The famous Broken Hill silver-lead ores were discovered in 1883 and production began in 1886. This produced an annual output of 50,000 tons by the 1890s. However, it was the enormous expansion of production in the Spanish mines and their ability – because of the free trade policies of successive British governments – to compete in the British home market that caused the collapse of the British lead mining industry. Because of cheap labour costs, low royalty payments, the accessibility of the mineral veins and the high silver content of the ores, Spain was able to produce lead much more cheaply than Britain. The result was that the price of lead fell from an average of £21 per ton in the 1850s to £9.50 per ton in the 1890s, a figure which was uneconomical for most British mines. During the period 1870-90 the output of the Spanish mines *increased* from 90,000 tons to 178,000 tons per annum; the output of the British mines *decreased* from 74,000 tons to 34,000 tons per annum. Fortunately, for those mines in a position to benefit, the price of zinc increased and certain areas, such as the Nenthead district, were cushioned from the worst effects of the collapse of the lead industry. However, in Northumberland, Durham, Cumberland, Westmorland, Yorkshire, Shropshire, Somerset, Devon, Cornwall and much of Wales lead mining practically ceased.

As with the British lead industry in general, the northern orefield never recovered after this major setback at the end of the nineteenth century. The Weardale Lead Company took over the old mines of the Beaumont Company in Weardale and East Allendale and their mine at Boltsburn became the largest lead mine in the country. The Belgian firm of Vieille Montagne Zinc based in Nenthead mined zinc blende in the Nent valley and in West Allendale. Barites was mined at Cow Green, Wiregill and other former lead mines in Teesdale. Settlingstones became the last witherite mine in the world, and fluorspar was mined from the old lead workings in Weardale and the Derwent valley.

Although mining continued until almost the end of the twentieth century, the great days of industrial activity were over. Depopulated villages, decaying farmsteads, ruined smelt mills, overgrown reservoirs and abandoned dressing floors became prominent features of the landscape. Unused pack horse tracks and dismantled railways systems scarred the countryside. All ghostly reminders of a once great industry and the community it created.

Butter tent at Burnfoot Show

Chapter Two

The Lead Mine

The art of prospecting has always been surrounded by mythology and there is much folklore associated with the discovery of lead and silver; but, because lead veins are invariably nearly vertical and in places reach the surface, the skill was in fact one of observation. Sometimes the vein was exposed by a stream or even by a heavy rainfall; but more often its presence was indicated by the discovery of particles of lead amongst the gravel of a neighbouring stream. This was known locally as *shoad ore* and it was once the custom in the mining districts for the men to go '*a-shoading*' after a storm: that is searching the rivers, streams and gullies for lead. Having found the shoad ore they then looked for the mineral vein by uncovering the vegetation from the ground in the neighbourhood of the find. This was often done by *trenching* but *hushing* was preferred where it was practicable. *Hushing* was carried out by collecting water behind a dam at the head of a gulley until a torrent could be released.

Forster, one of the most famous agents of the Blackett-Beaumont Company, described the result as follows:

> *"The torrent and the rush of stones wear out, not only the surface soil, but also a considerable depth of the superfices of the rock itself, and thus they discover and wash clean all the veins, the useful and the curious stones, etc, which lie in or across the line of the gutter. Valuable discoveries are often made in this way."*

Since most of the veins were known by the seventeenth century it is clear that these methods were successful.

During the eighteenth and nineteenth centuries, when long levels were constructed to drain or give access to the mines, new veins were discovered as the tunnelling progressed. The rich St Peters vein was found during the driving of the Blackett level which was designed to drain the great mine at Allenheads. A more successful method of exploring by levels was the cross cut level which was driven at right angles to the known vein. The miners were aware that the veins usually ran in a north-east to south-west or a north-west to south-east direction and parallel to one another, and by making a cross cut they hoped to discover a new vein. In 1822, the Coronation Vein was discovered in the Allercleugh cross-cut at the Allenheads mine. The flats associated with this vein in the Great Limestone were described by the agent William Crawhall as "in all probability... the richest length that was ever opened at Allenheads as a flat grove".

Miners at Work

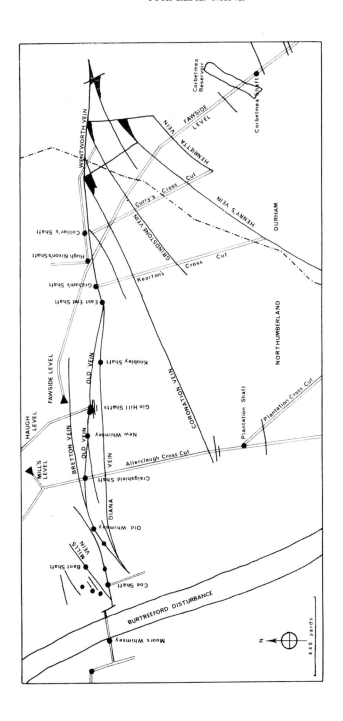

Allenheads Mine

The earliest method of mining was by bell pits, by which a shaft was sunk to a depth of about thirty feet and the ore was worked in both directions along the vein. Only a few yards could be worked before the roof became unsafe and the air impure. Then a new shaft was sunk and the mining continued. These early workings can be seen like traces of a gigantic mole, scarring the hillside. Perhaps the best place to see this feature is along the Sedling vein east of Cowshill.

The earliest tools of the miner were the pick, the hammer and the wedge – which meant that progress was slow until the introduction of gunpowder at the end of the seventeenth century. It was common practice to crack the rock by building a fire at the face and cooling it rapidly with water or vinegar, but this could be dangerous in badly ventilated mines. With the introduction of gunpowder, the construction of *adit* levels to drain the mines and the sinking of deeper shafts became more common. However, these developments principally belong to the eighteenth and nineteenth centuries after the formation of the larger companies which could afford the capital outlay necessary for such improvements.

Forster, describing the sinking of a shaft, noted that it was:

> *"in the first instance made square in shape, and sufficiently capacious to afford room for ladders, pumps, and the machinery which is required for raising to the surface the deads and the bouse. If it cannot be reached by one shaft another is put down. A horizontal gallery is opened at the bottom of the first shaft at the end of which a second shaft or sump is made...the shaft...will not require to be guarded within; but if the rock is soft and friable ... it is then necessary to support it, either with a wooden frame or a circular stone wall".*

Pigeon holes were left in the stone walls and *stemples* (wood grips) were fixed to enable the men to climb the shaft. Ladders later replaced stemples, which rotted too easily. At Allenheads cages were introduced in the mid-nineteenth century but this was unusual. Horse power was commonly used for haulage as the names Gin Hill shaft at Allenheads and Whimsey shaft at Coalcleugh indicate. Hydraulic power was used for haulage, both within the mine and to the surface, at the Burtree Pasture mine in Weardale and at other places. Steam powered haulage machinery – in common use on the neighbouring coalfield – was too extravagant in fuel to be used in the orefield. Easterby, Hall and Company did use steam engines for pumping and haulage in the Derwent valley at the beginning of the nineteenth century, but the experiment was short lived. The Derwent Company, which bought the mines, reverted to water power in 1810. Later in the century steam engines were again introduced, this time successfully.

Levels were preferred to *shafts* because the *deads* (the waste rock) and the *bouse* (the minerals) could be removed from the mine more easily. For this method a tunnel was constructed, usually in one of the softer layers of rock, sloping upwards at a gradient of about 1:250 to meet the mineral vein. The construction of these horse levels to give access to the mine coincided with the introduction of gunpowder, but progress was still slow and it was only the larger companies which were able to diversify their activities which could afford this unproductive work.

In 1684, the Blacketts began the Shieldridge level in their mine at Coalcleugh and at about the same time the Haugh level at Allenheads was started. The Barney Craig level was cut in 1760 at Coalcleugh and reached the mineral vein in 1808; while the Fawside level, begun in 1776, was to be the main entrance to the Allenheads mine in the nineteenth century. Wooden waggonways were laid in the levels which were later replaced by iron rails, first recorded at Coalcleugh in 1765. Horses were used for haulage.

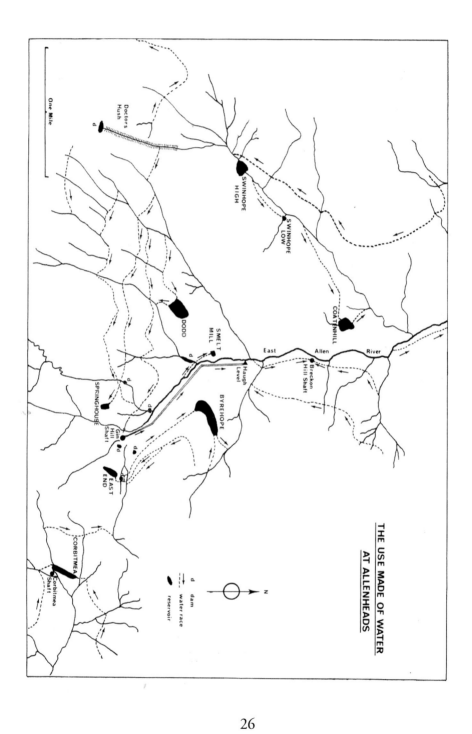

Levels had other advantages besides making access easier. They could also be used to drain a mine and there was always the possibility of striking a new vein. The Commissioners of Greenwich Hospital engaged John Smeaton, the builder of the Eddystone lighthouse, to design the Nentforce level to drain the mines in the Nent valley. The portal was in Alston near the railway station (where the level later supplied water for the locomotives) and it was driven 4.94 miles to the Brewery shaft at Nenthead mine. The first 3.5 miles to Nentsberry Haggs shaft were constructed as a canal on which barges thirty feet long were used to transport waste. Although work began in 1776, the mineral veins were not reached until the 1820s. Meanwhile, the London Lead Company the principal mining company in Nentdale, was spending between £6,000 and £7,000 per annum driving a network of levels in the Nenthead area. In 1854, the Blackett level was begun, to drain the East Allen valley. The drive was started simultaneously from Sipton Holmes Linn and Studdon Dene shafts and from the exit at Allendale Town. Only half of the nine miles was completed when the main drive ceased in 1896, and it had cost the Blackett-Beaumont Company £120,000. Had this ambitious plan been completed, it would have drained the Allenheads mine to the depth of the Scar Limestone. Neither in the driving of the Nentforce level nor the Blackett level were the dreams of rich new veins realised, although some worthwhile discoveries were made such as the St Peters vein at Sipton.

Where it was not possible to drain the mine using levels, hydraulic power was used. Westgarth Forster was the first engineer to develop the hydraulic engine which was installed underground at Coalcleugh in 1765. Others were built at Rampgill, Middle Cleugh, Tynebottom and Garrigill on Alston Moor shortly after. In the mid-nineteenth century, Thomas Sopwith, the chief agent at Allenheads, bought nine hydraulic pumps from the factory of his friend, William Armstrong. He installed two of these in the Fawside level for pumping; the others were used on the dressing floor at Allenheads or in the construction of the Blackett level.

Waterwheel at Brandon Walls

Ten reservoirs were built in the neighbourhood of Allenheads with a total capacity of 61,197,000 gallons. Water from the Corbetmea dam – situated in the Rookhope valley 1,614 feet above sea level – was fed down the Corbetmea shaft to the two Armstrong engines on the Fawside level. At Allenheads dressing floor, water discharged from the Fawside level was joined by water from other reservoirs and by water discharged from the surface engines. Here it was used for washing the ore before being led underground to drive four water wheels. One and a quarter miles away it was discharged from the Haugh level into the East Allen where it was joined by water from the smelt mill. Downstream, the river was diverted by races at various points to operate four corn mills and to drive machinery at Holmes Linn, Sipton and Breckon Hill on the Blackett level. Finally, north of Allendale Town, it was diverted to the Allen smelt mill and then discharged into the river. Water, that great enemy of the miner, was thus used as the main source of power – a good illustration of the ingenuity of the mining community.

Air in the Mines

The lead mines were fortunately free from *fire damp* (or methane gas) responsible for the major disasters in the neighbouring coalfield. However, the presence of *choke damp* or *stythe*, terms used to describe an atmosphere enriched with carbon dioxide and deficient in oxygen, made ventilation an important issue. When gunpowder was in use the atmosphere was further poisoned by fumes produced after firing. Air-borne dust produced by blasting and other mining operations also contaminated the atmosphere and was particularly dangerous if the dust contained silica particles.

In the coal mines the techniques of coursing the air through the mine were well developed by the early nineteenth century. This knowledge was applied to the lead mines where additional shafts or levels, trap doors, and – at Allenheads and Burtree Pasture – furnaces were used to aid ventilation. Water power was also used to supply air to the mine, and it is clear from Sopwith's account that it was a simple but efficient method:

"Among the improved methods of forcing pure air into lead mines, the water blast is found to be the most efficient. The contrivance simply consists of a wooden pipe placed in a shaft, and down which a stream of water is kept running, while a quantity of fresh air is carried with it. From the bottom of this wooden pipe, another pipe of wood, iron or lead is carried along the level, and the air being stopped by the water in the cistern at the bottom of the shaft and prevented from rising by the downward current of air and water, is forced along the pipe into the

workings of the mine. The water blast at the Nentberry engine shaft carries air along a leaden pipe 600 yards."

Techniques of Extraction

In lead mines the veins are mostly nearly vertical, and the techniques of extracting the ore are very different from the methods employed in a coal mine where the seams are almost horizontal. The main problem in the coal mine is to support the roof while the coal is being removed: in a lead mine the problem is to provide a floor to enable the miner to extract the ore. To solve this problem *sumps* or *winzes* (shafts sunk downwards) and *rises* or *raises* (shafts excavated upwards) were constructed from the horse level and new levels made above and below the main level.

Hand drilling at Smallcleugh Mine in 1897

78

Allenheads Leadmine Bargains Set Septem.r 27. 1850.

Isaac Varty & Lad Thomas Curry & Lad Thomas Reed & Lad	Isaac Varty (3 partners & 3 Lads) agree to raise Ore in their old ground in Henry's Vein @ 40/. per Bing till the 31st December next & to work five eight hour shifts per Week per man. Thomas Curry
Thomas Varty Thomas Shaw Rodger Shaw George Philipson	Thomas Varty (4 partners) agree to raise Ore in their old ground in Henry's Vein @ 34/. per Bing till the 31st December next. To Work five eight hour shifts per Week per man. Rodger Shaw
Thos. Robinson Thomas Craig Thomas Featherstone William Bell	Thomas Robinson (4 partners) agree to raise Ore in their old ground in Coronation Vein @ 40/. per Bing till the 31st December next & to Work five eight hour shifts per Week per man. Thos Craig
Isaac Craig William Cousin Pattinson White William Salkeld	Isaac Craig (4 partners) agree to raise Ore in their old ground in Coronation Vein @ 40/ per Bing till the 31st Decm.r next & to work five eight hour shifts per Week per man. Isaac Craig

31

Lead miners at Nenthead:
loading the spoil heaps for redressing, 1910

From all of these levels the miners could work either upwards or downwards by making use of *bunnings* – timber staging wedged between the vein walls in order to provide platforms. Working upwards, the miner removed the minerals until he could work no further, then a timber platform was erected and work continued. By repeating this procedure the miners could work up the vein, using the unwanted platforms to store the *deads* and dropping the *bouse* to the working level for transport to the surface. Working downwards, the miner removed the floor of the level for a set distance until he was unable to throw out to the working level. The procedure was repeated and once again the *deads* could be stored on the disused platforms. These *stopes*, or worked out *oreshoots*, containing *bunnings* supporting several hundred tons of *deads*, are the greatest hazard one can encounter when exploring old mines now that the timbers have rotted. Exploration is therefore best left to the professionals.

Miners' Pay

There were three methods of payment in the lead mines. A small number of men – joiners, blacksmiths, enginewrights, woodmen and stonemasons – were paid a daily rate or a weekly wage for their work. Those miners engaged in 'dead work' – driving levels, sinking shafts, cutting sumps and

A Partnership

rises – were paid so much per fathom (6ft; about 2m), according to their contract. The men actually working for the ore were paid at a certain price per *bing* of ore ready for delivery to the smelt mill, a *bing* being eight hundredweight (64st; 406.4k). The miners were organised into partnerships of two to twelve men and the partnership would enter into a bargain with the mine owner, usually through his agent, to raise ore at a certain price in a particular part of the mine. The price was fixed by the agent and varied according to the market price of lead at the time, and to the special circumstances of the part of the mine mentioned in the bargain. It was then up to the partnership to accept the bargain, to attempt to get it altered or to look for employment elsewhere.

Until the mid-nineteenth century, there was no restriction upon the hours of work and most men appear to have worked between six and eight hours per day. However, in the 1840s the contracts of the Blackett-Beaumont Company began to include the phrase "agree to work five eight hour shifts per week". The attempts of Thomas Sopwith to enforce these hours was the major cause of the strike at Allenheads in 1849, one of the few industrial disputes in the history of lead mining in the northern dales.

Wages varied according to the amount of work done and to the good fortune of the partnership. The bargain was – like mining itself – a calculated risk. The partnership could suffer because the quality of the vein had been overestimated, but it could also benefit if a rich oreshoot were discovered unexpectedly. In this way the miners shared in the gambling adventure of the industry but since the bargains were renegotiated every three months the rewards of good fortune were limited for the miners. Nonetheless, the gamble brought hope and excitement into the lives of the men and their families. Dr Mitchell, a member of the Children's Employment Commission, reported in 1842 that:

> "the lottery of the mine, like every other lottery, has a strong influence upon the mind... the large gains of the miners who are fortunate in falling in with rich ore in no way benefit the other men, except as affording them hope that one day it may so happen to them; but it is a delusive hope to many which is never realised".

Certainly, there were men who earned £60 and more each year but the vast majority earned less than half that amount.

Each adult was advanced a subsistence allowance which at Allenheads in 1842 was thirty shillings per month. This was known as "lent money" and at the end of the year the miner's account with the company had to be settled. If, after deducting the "lent money" and allowances for tools and powder, the men were in debt to the company the sum was usually waived or carried over to the next year's account. Those who had money to collect were able to enjoy the festivities of the 'great pays', or annual pay days.

Lodging Shop

The Dangers

All mining is dangerous: minor explosions, roof falls, flooding, suffocations and accidents with machinery did occur in the lead mines but they never resulted in the large scale loss of life which was common in the neighbouring coalfield. Respiratory diseases, caused through working in a dusty atmosphere made worse by the use of gunpowder, were widespread amongst the miners and resulted in premature death. The symptoms were described in 1864 by Dr Peacock when he reported to the Mines Commission a conversation he had had with some men from the Burtree Pasture mine:

> "They said that the bad air made them feel dizzy, sometime adding, 'as if they had been in liquor', caused violent headache, and made them feel sleepy, so that they could scarcely keep awake, and took all the power out of their limbs. Sometimes, they said, that they became quite faint; and I was told that they had occasionally 'fits' when working in bad air, and had to be carried out. Not infrequently they felt sick, and would vomit violently on coming to the surface; and they suffered from pains in the bowels, constipation or diarrhoea; were much prostrated, and had little or no apetite [sic] for their food on getting home."

It is evident from the doctor's account that the men were also suffering from lead poisoning.

Because of the remote position of the mines, some of the men had to walk a considerable distance, often more than three miles, to their work. For others the distance from home was too great and they were forced to seek lodgings near the mine in a neighbouring farmstead or at the company's lodging shop. Because of severe overcrowding and insanitary conditions in these lodging shops, they were considered with justification to be more harmful than the mines! The evidence of William Eddy to the Children's Employment Commission in 1842 supports this view:

"Our lodging-rooms were such as not to be fit for a swine to live in. In one house there were 16 bedsteads in the room upstairs, and 50 occupied these beds at the same time. We could not always get all in together but we got in when we could. Often three at a time in the bed and one at the foot. I have several times had to get out of bed and sit up all night, to make room for my little brothers, who were there as washers. There was not a single flag or board on the lower floor, and there were pools of water 12 inches deep. You might have taken a colrake (sic) and raked off the dirt and potato peeling six inches deep. At one time we had not a single coal. After I had been there two years, rules were laid down, and two men were appointed by the master to clean the house upstairs twice a week. The lower apartment was to be cleaned twice a day. Then the shop floor was boarded, and two tables were placed in the shop. After that two more shops were fitted up, but the increase of workmen more than kept up with the increased accommodation. The breathing at night when all were in bed was dreadful. The workmen received more harm from the sleeping-places than from the work."

By moving to the neighbouring Durham coalfield the lead miners might double their income, yet they preferred to stay in the dales. Undoubtedly, one reason was "their attachment to their native land and their own people which nothing can overcome", as Dr Mitchell noted in 1842. Another was the quality of the society to which they belonged – with its organised system of education and strong non-conformist religions. A third reason was the illusion that a rich strike would be made by the partnership in the near future: the gamble could someday pay off. However, the strongest reason was the degree of freedom which the lead miner enjoyed to work his own bargain, in his own time, by his own method. It is significant that the only serious strike to occur at Allenheads was in 1849 when the manager, Thomas Sopwith, attempted to introduce fixed working hours,

Entrance to Blackett Level, Allendale Town
See Route One

Chapter Three

The Dressing Floor

Bouse is the lead miner's term for the mixture of minerals extracted from the vein. Besides the lead ore, which is usually lead sulphide or galena, other minerals such as quartz, calcite, fluorspar, sphalerite, barites, witherite, and others less common than these are found in varying mixtures within the mineral vein. Indeed, the galena may constitute as little as 2% of the bouse. Even an extremely rich vein will consist of only about 50% galena.

The bouse was taken from the mine and placed in the bouse teems where the ore of different partnerships could be stored separately. This was necessary partly to enable the mine agents to calculate earnings and also to keep ore from different veins in the mine apart, which could be important to the smelters. On the dressing floor the galena was separated from the other minerals before being sent to the smelt mill.

Before the mechanisation of the processes on the dressing floor in the nineteenth century, the bouse was broken on a knockstone with a *bucker* – a thick iron plate about three inches square with a handle attached. Some of the ore was removed by picking at the bouse teems beforehand, and at the knockstone afterwards, but the majority of the ore was separated by means of a sieve. This was similar to a garden sieve and the crushed bouse on the sieve was agitated in a tub of water. The heavy galena fell to the bottom of the sieve, a mixture remained in the middle and the *dross* left on the top. The ore was then taken to the *bingstead*. The *chats* or the middle section was sieved again, while the dross was thrown onto the dead heap. The material which fell through the sieve into the tub was taken to the *buddle*.

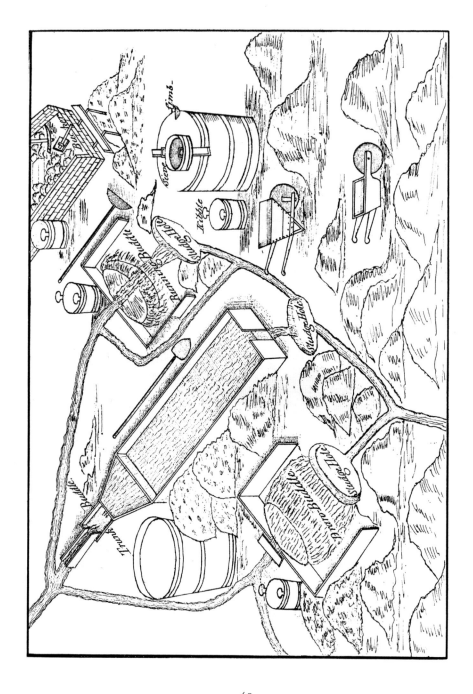

In its simplest form, the *buddle* was a plank of wood placed in a stream of water. Provided that the bouse was of a uniform size – the size of a hazel nut according to James Mulcaster, the chief smelter at Langley Mill – and provided the speed of the water was correct – the heavier galena would remain at the top of the buddle while the lighter waste was swept down. In the middle was a mixture called *chats* which had to be buddled again. The end product of these operations was not pure galena but lead concentrate which contained between 40% and 60% of lead ore.

The inefficiency of these early dressing methods meant that much of the ore was discarded in error. Because of this it was common practice to dump the *deads* into a *hush* or a gully and to use the head of water from the hush dam to recover some of the discarded ore. This was in effect *buddling* on a large scale, the lighter waste material being swept away while the heavier galena remained at the foot of the gully. It was also regarded as a useful method of disposing of industrial waste!

During the late eighteenth and the early nineteenth centuries, the dressing of lead ore became more sophisticated and most of the processes were mechanised. These processes have been represented in the diagram opposite which is based on the accounts of James Mulcaster of Langley Mill and Westgarth Forster, the agent at Coalcleugh.

There were basically four operations: *picking, sieving, buddling* and *fine buddling*; each of these might involve several jobs. From these there were four classes of ore produced for the smelter: *shaddered* (or hand picked) ore, *sieve* ore, *smitham* (or *smiddum*) ore, and *slime* ore. However, it should be remembered that there were variations in practice depending upon the size of the mining company and the peculiarities of the *mastermen washers*.

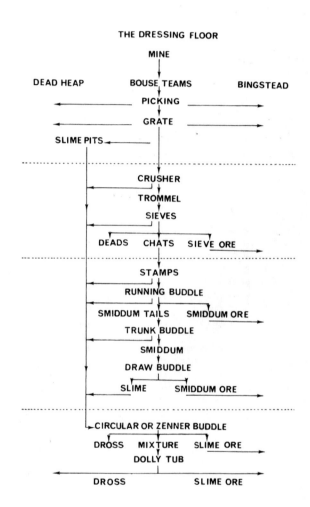

Flow chart of dressing floor processes

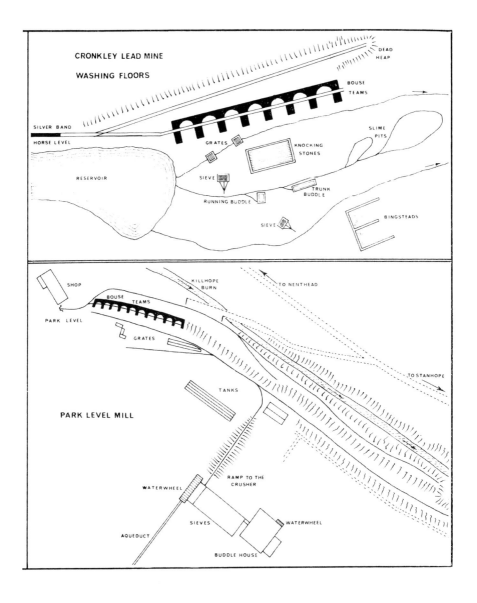

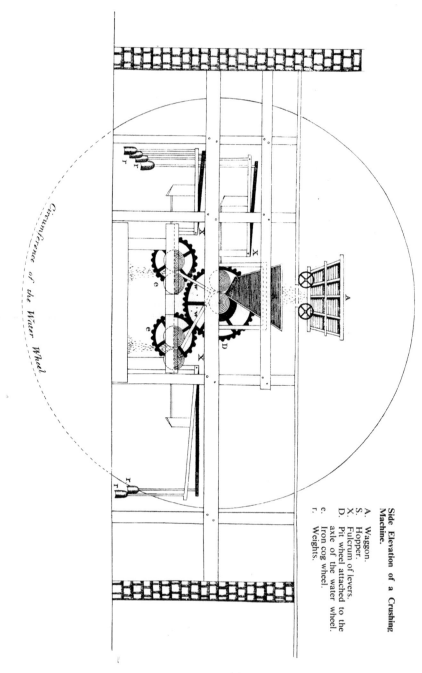

Circumference of the Water Wheel

Side Elevation of a Crushing Machine.

A. Waggon.
S. Hopper.
X. Fulcrum of levers.
D. Pit wheel attached to the axle of the water wheel.
e. Iron cog wheel.
r. Weights.

At the *bouse teems* obvious pieces of ore and waste were picked and wheeled to the *bingstead* and *dead heap* respectively. The remainder was sent to the *grate* upon which it was raked in a stream of water. This cleaned the bouse and enabled more hand picking to take place. The *bouse* which remained upon the grate, together with the smaller particles which had slipped through the grate and rolled into the pit beneath, was then sent to the grinder. Any ore which might have escaped with the stream of water was trapped in the *slime pit*.

In 1796 the *grinder* or *crushing mill* was introduced into the area by John Taylor, a Cornish miner, and by 1830 it was in use at all of the large mines and even in many of the smaller enterprises like those on Alston Moor. It was driven by water power and crushed the bouse to the consistency of gravel. The bouse then passed through a series of graduated cylinders where it was sorted into sizes and classified before being sieved. By this time a more sophisticated sieve had been invented, which could either be worked by a boy or attached to the grinder and operated mechanically. The bouse on the sieve was jerked up and down in a tank of water until the heavier galena fell to the bottom of the sieve and the waste accumulated at the top. The *chats*, or mixture in the centre, was sent to the *stampers* to be crushed before buddling; the sieve ore was taken to the bingsteads, to be transported to the smelt mill; the waste was dumped on the dead heap. The slime which had fallen through the sieve was collected in the slime pit. This process was termed "*jigging*".

The crushed chats were sent from the stampers first to the running buddle where a strong lad placed a suitable quantity on the large flagstone and then,

45

"allowing a strong current of water to flow over the flagstone from back to front, he draws the smiddum through it by means of a col-rake (coal-rake). During this operation, which is performed very slowly, the water carries away the comparatively light dross and a little of the ore, but leaves the great bulk of the ore in a pure state on the flagstone, when it is taken to the bingstead. The dross with its small admixture of ore, is called smiddum tails. It is wheeled to a square box (the trunk buddle) into which a strong stream of water falls, where it is agitated with a shovel until the slime which it contains is set free and swept away into the slime-pit below the box by the stream".

The *smiddum* was now sent to the draw buddle where the washer, standing on a board, raked it into the stream of water to recover the remaining smiddum ore. The slime was collected in a sludge hole.

Slime – the name given to the smallest particles of ore – had been collecting during all of the operations involving the use of water: grating, grinding, sifting, stamping and buddling. The slime ore was first separated from the slimy mixture of minerals in either a *circular* buddle or a *zenner* buddle.

The circular buddle

"has a circular floor which rises rapidly from the circumference to the centre. In the centre is fixed a metal pillar, about four feet in height, which serves the double purpose of a support for the funnel shaped box and an axis upon which a fan shaped wheel, fixed within the box, revolves. A stream of water being turned into this box, and its outflow being so regulated that the box is always kept full, a quantity of sludge, or slime, is next put into it. In its progress downwards the sludge is thoroughly mixed with the water by the revolution of the wheel. Passing through the narrow opening at the bottom of the box, the mixture,

46

in its progress from the centre to the circumference is equally diffused over the floor. In the case of the circular buddle the dross is carried near to, or even over, the edge of the floor, whilst the pure ore, owing to its greater specific gravity lodges near the centre... The worthless dross which lies near the edge of the floor...is taken away, then that portion which consists of a mixture of dross and ore, and lastly the pure ore."

The *zenner* buddle was very similar in construction except that the floor rotated and the ore, mixtures and dross were collected in four compartments around the circumference.

The mixtures from the circular and zenner buddles were sent to the dolly tub where the separation of the finest particles took place:

"The tub is first filled to a certain height with water; the dolly is then introduced and turned quickly round, a circular motion being thus communicated to the water: in the meantime a suitable quantity of slime ore is slowly put in. When the ore is thoroughly mixed the dolly is withdrawn, and the workmen then proceed to beat the sides of the tub with a hammer or a heavy piece of wood, in order to keep the matter in suspension as long as possible and thus allow it to settle gradually. The ore being heavier finds its way to the bottom through the force of gravity and the light refuse settles upon it. The water is then let out, and the dross removed to the dead heap. The pure ore at the bottom of the tub is taken to the bingstead."

The mechanisation of the dressing floor was accomplished in the early nineteenth century. Improvements particularly in the treatment of the finer ore – such as the *Brunton belt* invented at Allenheads in 1847 or the *slime trunking machine* invented by Attwood at Nenthead in 1849 – continued to be made. However, despite the use of hydraulic separators and vanning tables such as those used at Nenthead and Sipton in the twentieth century, the basic tasks remained the same and the principles of dressing the ore were fully understood by the mid-nineteenth century.

Better dressing methods (and therefore an increased yield of ore from the bouse) resulted in greater profits for those who could afford to mechanise. It made it possible to work low quality veins which had previously been non-wageable, and even the deads from former mining operations could now be re-dressed with profit. It is, however, important to realise that the sophisticated methods of the Blackett-Beaumont Company and the London Lead Company were not universally adopted, and many miners on Alston Moor continued to use the older practices.

Boys in the Lead Mines

In the eighteenth century women had worked on the dressing floor. However, by the nineteenth century it was considered improper in the northern Pennines to engage women as washers, although they were employed in Yorkshire and in other mining areas. The work was reserved for only the men and boys.

Two mastermen washers were in charge of eight boys who were paid according to their age and the number of hours they worked. The youngest boys, aged between nine and eleven years, were employed at the grate picking out stones and the ore. After the first year they were given heavier work such as wheeling the bouse onto the grate and wheeling the deads into the hush. In their fourth year they graduated to jigging and in later years to using the buddle. After seven years on the dressing floor, by which time they would become familiar with the minerals extracted from the mine, the boys were either employed as mastermen washers or taken into the mines as a member of a partnership. The number of groups engaged in washing depended upon the size of the washing floor: at large establishments like Nenthead, Coalcleugh, Allenheads, and Burtree Pasture more than a hundred were employed. The following table from the report of J R Liefchild to the Children's Employment Commission of 1842 gives some details of the ages, the hours of work and the wages of one group of washers in the Beaumont mines.

The operations on the dressing floor depended upon the continuous supply of running water which, because of the building of reservoirs, was unlikely to be interrupted except by very severe drought in summer. However, in winter all work was stopped when the frosts arrived. During the winter months – usually from November to April – the older boys were taken into the mines and the younger boys were sent to one of the many schools in the area. Education was provided by the mining companies – assisted by the Bishop of Durham and the Commissioners of Greenwich Hospital – long before it became available to most working class children elsewhere in the country. This explains why, in 1842, Dr Mitchell was

Masterman Washers—EDWARD HEWITSON, JOHN LEE									
		Days in each week				Total Days in each Month	Rate of wages per day	Amount	Cash advanced per Month
Age	Names	April 10, 1841	April 17, 1841	April 24, 1841	May 1, 1841				
Yrs. Mths.							d.	£. s. d.	£. s. d.
16 2	Anthony Johnson	4	5½	5½	5½	20½	15	1 5 7	1 0 0
17 2	John Chatt	2	5½	5½	5½	18½	16	1 4 8	1 0 0
14 1	William Coats	4	5½	5	5	19½	13	1 1 1	0 15 0
12 11	John Snaith	4	5	5½	3	17½	9	0 13 1	0 10 0
12 11	William Dixon	4	5½	5½	5½	20½	9	0 15 4	0 10 0
10 9	John Robson	4	5½	5½	5½	20½	7	0 11 11	0 10 0
11 9	Dawson Whitfield	4	3	3	5	15	6	0 7 6	0 10 0
16 2	Michael Stobbs	4	5½	5½	6	21	9	0 15 9	0 10 0

able to describe the population of the dales as "well educated, and of intellectual capacity and acquirement surpassing any I have ever met with in England".

In comparison with their contemporaries in the coalfield or in the cotton industry, the lot of the washerboys was an enviable one. They were generally expected to work from seven in the morning till seven in the evening with an hour's break for lunch. However, on Saturdays, they worked only half a day. The work was not dangerous but it could be unpleasant, particularly in cold or wet weather since it was unusual for the boys to have any shelter from the wind and the rain. One washerboy, Levi Salkeld, described to the Commissioners in 1842, that "the boys sometimes thumped me when I was washing because I did not behave myself, and because I called them by-names, and sometimes I did not work hard enough". However, cruelty towards children, which is frequently mentioned in the reports of children working in the coal mines and cotton mills, was never observed by the Commissioners during their visits to the lead dales.

The washerboys sometimes had to work in remote places and stay in the lodging shops which – as for the miners – was their most unpleasant and dangerous experience. Matthew Dowson described his experience:

> " [I] went on Monday morning, and took... bread, white and brown, potatoes, bacon callop half a pound, coffee an ounce, and sugar half a pound and that supplied me till Saturday at twelve. I took with me three pints of milk and we kept it up the level a little to preserve it sweet. I lodged in one of the shops... 21 of us slept in the same room; there were twelve beds; there was a bad smell."

Despite having to work in the rain and on occasion stay at the lodging shop, the children in the dales had a much better existence than did most of their contemporaries: they worked hard but for reasonable hours and for a reasonable reward. They were disciplined but were not cruelly treated, and they were given an education at day school and Sunday school.

Most important of all, they had time to enjoy themselves as Stephen Collingwood, a washerboy of fifteen described:

"The boys play at marbles and jack-ball; we strike it against the wall; we play at cricket and football; I often go fishing in the river, and catch trout; I never go bird-nesting."

Boys at the water pump

Children playing

Chapter Four

The Smelt Mill

The most common lead ore found in the northern orefield is galena or lead sulphide although occasionally lead carbonate or *cerussite* was mined, as for example in the Hudgill Burn area of Alston Moor. The lead contains varying proportions of silver and other less valuable impurities such as antimony and arsenic. In medieval times the techniques of smelting were primitive: the lead ore was simply roasted with wood near the top of an exposed hill and the prevailing wind was used to provide the blast. Such sites were known as bale hills and place-name evidence for their position is common in the north, for example Bale Hill House near Blanchland.

Smelt Mill at Blackton

By the eighteenth century, the smelter's art was more sophisticated: it involved the ability to judge the correct ratio of fuel to ore and the skill to assess the varying temperatures needed not only for the different ores to be smelted but also for the different stages in the smelting process. Equally, there was an art to maintaining a constant blast of air, equally distributed over the hearth. The whole process relied for its success upon the ability of experienced craftsmen and for this reason it was never mechanised. The account which follows is based on the description of James Mulcaster of Langley Mill, Westgarth Forster of Coalcleugh and Hugh Lee Pattinson of Blaydon refinery, the founder of the Washington Chemical Company.

Early in the nineteenth century, the practice of roasting the ore before smelting, in a reverberatory furnace with a current of air passing over it, was developed at Langley. The galena was converted in part to lead oxide and in part to lead sulphate:

$$i. \quad 2PbS + 3O_2 = 2PbO + 2SO_2$$
$$ii. \quad PbS + 2O_2 = PbSO_4$$

The purpose of this operation was to remove some of the sulphur and antimony before smelting began. The process was also used to cake the finest ores, such as the slime ore from the dolly tubs, and to cake the ore particles collected after the cleaning of the smelt mill flues. The Blackett-Beaumont Company believed that roasting enabled the smelter ultimately to produce more lead from a given quantity of ore. About half a ton was roasted at each charge and there were three charges during an eight hour shift. Particular care had to be taken to see that the ore was not over-heated: when it became clammy, the surface was raked to expose new ore to the air and flame.

There were two types of furnaces used for smelting lead: the *ore hearth* in which the ore and the fuel were mixed and the larger, *reverberatory furnace* in which the ore and the fuel were kept separate. The reverberatory furnace produced a better grade of lead but it had certain disadvantages, which explains why it was not widely adopted for smelting in the northern orefield although it *was* used for roasting lead ore, refining litharge and

Elevation of an Ore Hearth.

a. hearth (24″ × 12″ ⋅ 24″).
b. arched hood to carry away fumes.
c. workstone.
d. lead pot.
e. backstone.
f. pipe stone.
g. bearers.

softening hard lead. It required coal as a fuel, which was expensive in the lead dales, whereas peat from the moorland could be used in the ore hearths. Furthermore, the ore hearth was more suited to smelt lower grade ores and small quantities of ore.

In the ore hearth the roasted ore, which was a mixture of galena, lead oxide and lead sulphate, was heated over a current of air. Within the furnace several chemical reactions were taking place simultaneously. First, the lead

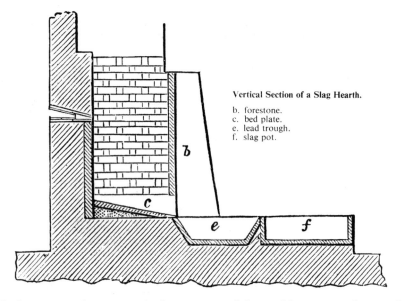

Vertical Section of a Slag Hearth.

b. forestone.
c. bed plate.
e. lead trough.
f. slag pot.

sulphide was combining with the oxygen of the air blast to produce either lead oxide and sulphur dioxide, or lead sulphate:

i. $\quad 2PbS + 3O_2 = 2PbO + 2SO_2$

ii. $\quad PbS + 2O_2 = PbSO_4$

Secondly, the lead oxide and lead sulphate were combining with the galena to produce lead and sulphur dioxide:

i. $\quad 2PbO + PbS = 3Pb + SO_2$

ii. $\quad PbSO_4 + PbS = 2Pb + 2SO_2$

Thirdly, some of the lead sulphate and lead oxide were combining with the carbon, either from the peat or the coal, to form lead, carbon dioxide and sulphur dioxide:

i. $\quad 2PbO + C = 2Pb + CO_2$

ii. $\quad PbSO_4 + C = Pb + SO_2 + CO_2$

Fourth, the other impurities in the lead ore formed a grey slag which was skimmed off and later smelted in the slag hearth. The method of working the ore hearth furnace – which employed two men – is described by Dr Greenwood in 1875:

"...the rectangular cavity or chamber (a) is filled with peat...an ignited peat is then placed in front of the twyer, and the blast turned on, whereby combustion rapidly spreads throughout the furnace, upon which a little coal is added, and shortly afterwards a small portion of the partially reduced ore mixed with slag and cinders, which remain upon the hearth at the end of each shift, and which is technically known as browse or bouse, is thrown into the hearth, when, after the lapse of half an hour... the contents of the hearth are stirred up and a portion of the charge is thrown forward on to the work-stone (c), and any grey slag is separated... the working requires a careful manipulation of the peats which are judiciously placed before the twyer, so as to distribute the blast uniformly over the hearth, while the ore or bouse is added to the furnace charge in small quantities at a time, always introducing it on to that part of the hearth which appears hottest, when the work then proceeds regularly, with the introduction of peat fuel and bouse as required, the workmen stirring the charge with iron bars at intervals of about five minutes; whilst at intervals of about twenty minutes they throw forward a portion of the charge on to the work-stone for the separation, as before, of the grey slag, and to permit the breaking up of any browse which may have collected; after which the browse, with a certain quantity of coal and quick lime, is returned to the furnace, and a fresh supply of raw or roasted ore is placed on top while at the same time another workman introduces his bar into the furnace and detaches any slag, etc, that may have attached itself to the twyer. Lead is now freely reduced from the ore, and collects at the bottom of the hearth, which it soon overflows, and

passes along the gutter or channel in the middle of the work-stone into the kettle or lead pot (d), which when full is skimmed and the metal ladled out into moulds forming pig-lead. In a shift of from twelve hours to fourteen hours the above furnace will yield about 2.5 tons of lead."

The grey slag produced by the ore hearth contains about 10% of the total amount of the lead in the ore. It is sent to the stamp mill to be crushed before being re-smelted on the slag hearth, a worthwhile task because about 30% of the slag is lead which can be recovered. The slag hearth is a small blast furnace where the ore is heated at a much higher temperature in order to release the metal. The chemical reactions were the same as the complex series described for the ore hearth – in this case the most common reaction being the lead sulphate and lead oxide combining with the carbon of the coke to form lead, sulphur dioxide and carbon dioxide. The impurities remained as a black slag. Westgarth Forster describes the operation of the furnace:

"The interior is filled up to the height of seventeen inches that is to within two inches of the blast-pipe, with ashy cinders, beaten closely together. The pot, for the reception of the lead, is also filled with these cinders, which, in each case, answer the purpose of a filter. A little waste wood, or peat, is placed inside the hearth, and upon this is thrown a shovelful of burning coals; the blast is then turned on. When sufficient heat has been obtained, coke is thrown upon the wood, and over all is spread a stratum of grey slag, or whatever other matter is to be smelted. From time to time, as occasion requires, the grey slag and coke are added. In this process the slag is made perfectly fluid as well as the lead. The latter separates from the former, by finding its way through the filter of ashy cinders, which the former cannot do because of its viscidity. At the very moment when the slag becomes molten upon the filter (which is

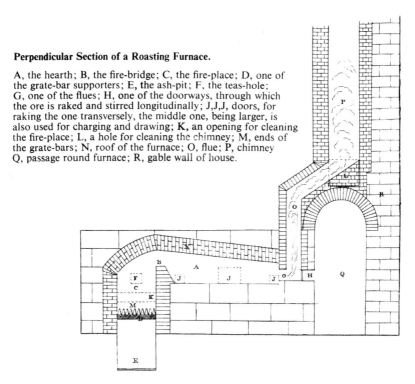

Perpendicular Section of a Roasting Furnace.

A, the hearth; B, the fire-bridge; C, the fire-place; D, one of the grate-bar supporters; E, the ash-pit; F, the teas-hole; G, one of the flues; H, one of the doorways, through which the ore is raked and stirred longitudinally; J,J,J, doors, for raking the one transversely, the middle one, being larger, is also used for charging and drawing; K, an opening for cleaning the fire-place; L, a hole for cleaning the chimney; M, ends of the grate-bars; N, roof of the furnace; O, flue; P, chimney Q, passage round furnace; R, gable wall of house.

soon after the commencement of the shift), the workman makes a hole through the latter about an inch in diameter, with a poker, through which the molten slag flows in a red hot stream, and after passing over the lead pot, which is placed between the hearths and the cistern, falls into the latter. The lead obtained by slag-hearth smelting, is not so pure as that obtained from the ore hearth. It is never so entirely freed from the mineralizing substance, and it is hardened by the carbon of the coke. The former should never be used but in cases where the latter fails, or is extremely slow in smelting the carbonates."

In 1816 William Hall of Blaydon patented a method of softening *hard* lead, lead which was unsuitable for industrial purposes because it lacked malleability. The hard lead was heated above its melting point in a type of reverberatory furnace, the impurities were oxidised and collected as a slag on the surface of the metal. The temperature was lowered, the slag skimmed off and the softness of the lead tested. This procedure was repeated until the lead became malleable – the time required varied from one day to two weeks, depending on the hardness of the lead. The softening of the exceptionally hard Spanish leads which were rich in silver (they contained about fifty ounces per ton of ore) became an important industry on Tyneside during the second half of the nineteenth century. Coal was exported from the Tyne to smelt the ores in eastern Spain and the colliers carried the hard leads to be softened and refined as ballast on the return journey. In 1862, Newcastle imported 12,459 tons of lead which yielded approximately 600,000 ounces of silver – this was more than the total production of all the British mines.

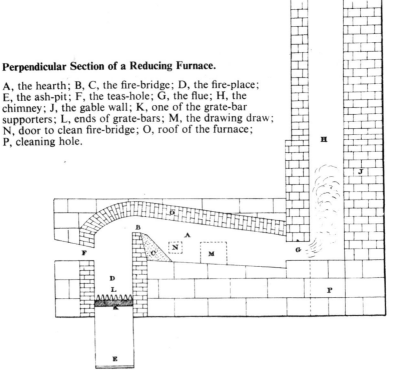

Perpendicular Section of a Reducing Furnace.

A, the hearth; B, C, the fire-bridge; D, the fire-place; E, the ash-pit; F, the teas-hole; G, the flue; H, the chimney; J, the gable wall; K, one of the grate-bar supporters; L, ends of grate-bars; M, the drawing draw; N, door to clean fire-bridge; O, roof of the furnace; P, cleaning hole.

All galena contains silver in varying proportions, and the extraction of this valuable metal was always an important aspect of the lead industry. Until the development of the crystallisation process during the years 1829-33 by Hugh Lee Pattinson at Blaydon, the only method of extracting the silver was by cupellation whereby the lead and other impurities were oxidised from the silver by the action of heat and air. The only improvement since ancient times was the adaptation of the reverberatory furnace to refining, which was capable of handling larger quantities. There were two stages in the *cupellation* process: the concentration stage to increase the amount of silver in the lead from about ten ounces to two hundred and fifty ounces per ton of metal, and the *refining* process to complete the separation. Westgarth Forster gives a detailed description of this method:

> *"The test frame is filled with a mixture of bone and pearl ash, beaten very closely together with flat-headed iron beaters, the heads of which are about two inches in diameter. The pearl ash has the property of semi-vitrifying the bone ashes or destroying their friability, and making them more durable. The ashes are then scooped out with a small spade, made for that purpose, until there is left upon the test-frame and upon the sides a coating of about an inch and a half to two inches thick, excepting in the forepart, called the breast where the coating is twelve inches. In the breast a channel is cut from the inner side of the frame, one inch and a quarter in width and nine inches long, with which a passage, or gateway, for the litharge communicates.*
>
> *The test thus prepared is placed in the refining furnace and is supported at a proper height against, or close to, an iron ring, which runs around the furnace. The height of the furnace roof from this ring is fifteen inches at the fire bridge side and twelve inches at the flue.*

The fire must be applied to the test very cautiously, because an intense heat evaporates the water, with which the ashes were moistened, too rapidly, and causes the test to fly to pieces. When the test has been slowly brought to a reddish heat, it is nearly filled with melted lead, previously fused in a cast-iron pot, five hundredweight being required for the purpose. The lead soon becomes covered with a grey pellicle, called dross, which is a mixture of the first oxide of metallic lead. After the heat of the furnace has been intensified, the lead becomes of a whiteish-red colour, and the whole surface covered with litharge... The blast is then made to play upon the surface of the lead from the hind part of the test, and thus force the litharge up to the breast, and over the gateway whence it falls upon a cast iron plate in clods, in which state it is taken to the reducing furnace to be re-converted into lead.

"The blast of air, not only acts mechanically by sweeping off the litharge from the surface of the lead, but also furnishes enough oxygen for its formation, the refiner taking care to command the proper heat. As the surface of the lead must necessarily become depressed by its oxidizement [sic] to, or below, the level of the gateway, more lead is allowed to flow in from the melting pot in order to raise it to its proper height. The operation is continued in this manner until the workmen consider that the lead which is left in the bottom of the pan is too rich for proper and easy management. This rich lead is therefore taken out of the test. After such a quantity of rich lead has been obtained as, by assay, is found-to contain sufficient silver for a cake, it is melted down again, and the silver obtained in a test. The cake of silver weighed between 5,000 and 7,000 ounces. It was removed from the test, cut up into pieces, melted and cast into ingots."

The litharge or lead oxide was usually converted into lead in a reducing furnace (another adaptation of the reverberatory furnace) using coal as the reducing agent:

$$2PbO + C = 2Pb + CO_2$$

Sometimes there was a market for the litharge in the developing chemical industry on Tyneside where it was used in the manufacture of pigments for the paint and glass industries and in the production of caustic soda. The close association between the lead and chemical industries of Tyneside is exemplified by the career of Hugh Lee Pattinson who was born at Alston in 1796 and educated at the village school. For four years he was a clerk at the Ouseburn soap works before being appointed *assayer* at Langley Mill in 1825. He moved to work for the Beaumonts and developed the crystallisation process at the Blaydon refinery between 1829 and 1833. With the royalties from this invention he began the Felling Chemical Works in partnership with John Lee in 1834 and in 1842 he founded the Washington Chemical Company. Many scientific honours including a Fellowship of the Royal Society were bestowed on Pattinson before his death at West Boldon in 1858.

The Pattinson process was an alternative method of concentrating the amount of silver in the lead before refining. A series of from seven to eleven hemispherical cast-iron pots, about five feet in diameter and capable of holding about nine tons of metal were arranged in a row along one side of the refinery. Each pot was heated by its own fire which was controlled by an independent damper so that any pot could be cooled without interfering with the remainder. In addition to the lead pots, there was a series of smaller wash pots for cleaning the crystallising ladle.

A charge of about seven tons was placed in the middle pot and melted as rapidly as possible. The surface of the metal was cleaned by removing the oxides with the perforated ladle and the whole pot was allowed to cool slowly. Since lead crystallises before silver, it could be removed. The lead crystals were placed in the pot on the right and the silver rich lead placed in the pot on the left. The process was repeated and in every case the impoverished crystals were transferred to the next pot on the right while the enriched lead was transferred to the next pot on the left. Ultimately, the pot on the extreme right contained the purest lead and the post on the extreme left contained lead with a silver concentration of about 250 ounces per ton which was suitable for cupellation.

Pattinson Pots

The Pattinson process made it possible to extract silver from ores which contained as little as two ounces per ton of lead while it was considered necessary to have at least eight ounces per ton to make extraction profitable by cupellation alone. Furthermore, the quality of the lead produced was improved since more of the impurities were removed, not just silver but antimony, nickel, arsenic and others. A very rich lead for cupellation was manufactured without wastage through the production of litharge which, by the traditional method, had to be later reduced back to lead. The process was quickly adopted throughout the northern Pennines and although several minor improvements were made, notably by Pattinson's friend Joseph Stagg, the manager of the Nenthead mill, Pattinson's process remained the favourite refining method.

Smelters as 'aristocrats'

In several ways, the smelters represented an aristocracy among the working classes in the dales. They were few in number and their exclusiveness was accentuated by the custom of retaining the skills within a family group. After working on the dressing floor, the smelter's son became a labourer at the smelt mill at about the age of eighteen where in the course of time he was taught the various arts of smelting and ultimately of refining, the most skilled job of all. This education was not confined to practical experience under the watchful eye of a master smelter; promising young men received instruction from Professor Johnson, Reader in Chemistry in the University of Durham, and Dr Thomas Richardson, Lecturer in Chemistry at the College of Medicine in Newcastle. The smelters were paid piece rates which varied according to the quality of the ore which had to be smelted. Although there is very little information about their earnings, it is evident from what does survive that they were considerably more than the wages of the miners. In 1809 the men at the Allen mill at Catton were earning 14/6d per week and in 1842 George Metcalf, giving evidence to the Children's Employment Commission reported that the smelters "get from 15/- to 16/- a week". The companies offered special inducements to retain the services of these skilled men who were always vulnerable to offers from rival concerns. At Nenthead, the smelters were provided with better housing than the miners which can still be seen today in Hillersdon Terrace; at Langley the smelters were given land for smallholdings.

Smelters at Work

There was considerable variation in the working arrangements at the different mills as the following remarks of Hugh Lee Pattinson indicate:

"At mills where the smelting shift is 12 hours, the hearths usually go on 12 hours, and are suspended 5... The two men who manage the hearth, each work four shifts per week; terminating their weeks work at three o'clock on Wednesday afternoon. They are succeeded by two other men, who also work four twelve hour shifts; the last of which they finish at four o'clock on Saturday. In these eight shifts from 36 to 40 bings of ore are smelted, which, when of good quality, produce from 9 to 10 fodders

of lead. At other mills where the shift is from fourteen to fifteen hours, the furnace is kindled at four o'clock in the morning, and worked until six in the evening each day, six days in the week … Almost at every smelting mill a different mode of working, in point of time and quality, is pursued."

Not only did the smelting arrangements differ from one mill to another but at the same mill men were engaged in different jobs and would work different shifts, dictated by the nature of their work. William Walton, giving evidence to Dr Mitchell, reported that while at the smelting furnace "we are ten hours on and twenty hours off, and go on day and night from one o'clock on Monday morning to two on Saturday afternoon". However, when roasting ore, "we are eight hours on and eight hours off all the week, and whole six days from six on Monday to two on Saturday afternoon, day and night, that the furnaces might not cool which would lose a great deal of time".

A variety of very harmful by-products were released into the atmosphere as a result of roasting, smelting and refining lead ore, which were injurious both to the workers and to the neighbourhood. Lead, antimony, arsenic and sulphuric acid were all produced, and before the building of the long smelt flues in the early nineteenth century the mill must have been a most unpleasant and dangerous place to work. At Langley there was considerable opposition from the local farmers whose animals and lands were poisoned by the gasses from the mill. In 1779 the Commissioners paid compensation of over £175 to men like the tenant of Langley Castle farm who, in the previous ten years, had lost eight Galloways (ponies), five horses, three cows and numerous sheep. The village of Dirt Pot, the site of the Allenheads mill, has a tellingly descriptive name. Dr Mitchell reported that the smoke from the smelt mill at Nenthead was 'most offensive to travellers, and in a populous district would not be endured half an hour'.

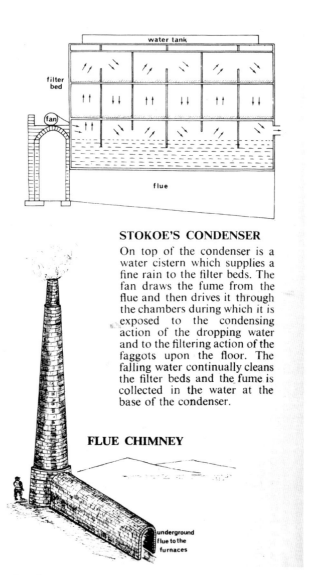

STOKOE'S CONDENSER

On top of the condenser is a water cistern which supplies a fine rain to the filter beds. The fan draws the fume from the flue and then drives it through the chambers during which it is exposed to the condensing action of the dropping water and to the filtering action of the faggots upon the floor. The falling water continually cleans the filter beds and the fume is collected in the water at the base of the condenser.

FLUE CHIMNEY

Nevertheless, by the mid-nineteenth century, the general opinion was that a well ventilated mill was a much more healthy environment than were the mines. This was the result of the building of long flues which was undertaken not entirely for humanitarian reasons as the evidence of John Robinson, the agent of the Derwent Lead Company indicates:

"To save the surface of the land from injury, we carry from the smelting hearths a tunnel arched a mile long, and let the smoke up by a chimney. At the end of the year, we clean the chimney, and smelt the matter obtained, called fume, and get from this a great quantity of lead, sufficient to remunerate for the expenses of making the tunnel, and yield a profit besides."

Remains of flue showing cross-section, above Allendale

The fume (or the solid particles carried by the draught from the furnace but not the smoke) could be trapped in a condenser, which was particularly useful in areas where it was impossible to construct a long flue. At Nenthead, the manager of the mill, Joseph Stagg, invented a condenser which forced the fume through water which held the particles in suspension but allowed the gases to escape. The fume was later separated in collecting tanks. A variation was developed by Mr Stokoe at Langley where the fumes were driven by a fan blast through a series of columns down which a stream of water fell to condense the fumes. The water was collected in tanks and the fume separated.

Chapter Five

The Landscape

"This country, though politically distributed among three counties, is one and the same in all its characteristic features. From it flow the Tyne, the Wear and the Tees, and many branches which fall into these rivers. Along the banks of these, and several smaller streams which fall into them, are dales or valleys, cultivated near the banks, and for a short distance up the sides of the hills; but soon cultivation and enclosure cease, and beyond them rise dark fells, covered with peat moss and heath; and between one vale and another is a wide extent of high moorland, extending sometimes for a dozen miles. In these upland tracts are no inhabitated [sic] houses, but thousands of black-faced sheep are scattered over them; and these breed the grouse which attract the sportsman at the proper season of the year to this country."

Dr Mitchell's description of the lead dales of northern England could well have been written today by a person walking the Pennine Way up the South Tyne valley, over Cross Fell and on through Teesdale. Having tramped through the Cheviot Hills and the wasteland of western Northumberland the modern traveller will be impressed by the number of villages, scattered farmsteads and industrial remains in the lead dales. If the weather is at all normal for August, he will be wet and cold and perhaps forced to wonder why, of all the places on earth, people should build houses at Nenthead, Garrigill, Langdon Beck or at any of the other settlements in the area. The answer is entirely geological – the presence of mineral wealth resulted in the building of settlements at heights between one and two thousand feet above sea level in the northern Pennines. By contrast, in the Cheviots where there are no mineral deposits, farmsteads are rarely found above seven hundred feet. Alston claims to be the highest market town in England, the road from Nenthead to Weardale the highest major road in England, the track which once passed over Bolts Law into Rookhope the highest point reached by a railway in England ... all of these were a result of the exploitation of the rich lead veins in the region.

The landscape is scarred with evidence of mining activity which has been described in detail in the previous chapters: the mine, the dressing floor and the smelt mill. In addition to these extensive remains (which belong principally to the great period of activity in the eighteenth and nineteenth centuries) traces of the old pack horse tracks, the turnpike roads and the narrow and standard gauge railways can be found. The roads have survived but the railways and the pack horse tracks are largely decayed. The scattered settlements of the mining community with their small fields enclosed from the moorland waste are mainly re-used as additional farm buildings or weekend cottages; also in the mining centres – such as Allenheads and Nenthead which were once the capitals of the great mining companies – the community has shrunk. Nevertheless, the houses of the miners, their chapels and schools, largely built in the early nineteenth century, still exist as important archaeological evidence of the society which they served.

Transport

Transporting the ore from the mine to the smelt mill and the lead from the smelt mill to the warehouses at Newcastle and Stockton was a difficult task before the development of road and rail transport in the nineteenth century, because of the weight of the lead. The burden of it was not helped by the undulating nature of the countryside, the severity of the winters and the truculent nature of the carriers. Farmers from outside the mining districts – whose lands were able to support the large number of

Galloway ponies needed to provide transport for the lead industry – earned additional income by contracting to carry the lead to the ports. Such were the problems of hiring carriers that large landowners like the Blacketts and Greenwich Hospital, who also possessed estates in the neighbouring agricultural districts, were forced to *compel* their tenants to act as carriers. Each Galloway pony carried two hundredweight of lead across to the ports and on the return journey they brought coal for the smelt mill or provisions for the miners. Where it was practicable, small carts, carrying a bing (eight hundredweight of lead) and pulled by one Galloway, were used. The routes changed as the tracks became worn and impassable in wet weather or when the contract was given to a different carrier. Galloways continued to be used until the collapse of the industry, although on a more limited scale after the development of railways. Even today the tracks worn by these pack horses can be followed across the moors.

Transport in the Dales

Early in the 1820s John McAdam was commissioned by the Greenwich Hospital to survey the roads within an eighteen mile radius of Alston which contained most of the mining districts. His report, presented in July 1823, described the roads then existing as "altogether the worst that have yet come to my knowledge, not only have the old defective methods been followed in the formation, stoning, and subsequent repairs of the roads, but the work has been executed in the most slovenly careless manner, without method, and regardless of expense". He concluded that "under such circumstances it must be obvious that the traffic required by the Commerce and Agriculture of the District must be carried on with difficulty and at a great expense". The outcome of this report was that in the next decade the road system in the area was greatly improved and became, apart from some minor additions which were made later, the network which is in use today.

The Rookhope Incline

Canal transport was in use in the Nentforce level and there were several schemes to build a canal from Haydon Bridge to Blaydon. However, it was railways not canals which were to provide the solution to the transport problems of the lead industry. The mineral resources of Weardale had attracted the attention of the promoters of the Stockton and Darlington Railway as early as 1822, but it was not until the building of the Haggarsleazes branch in 1830 that Weardale lead was carried by the Stockton and Darlington Railway to the warehouses at Stockton. The opening of the Stanhope and Tyne Railway in 1834 enabled lime and lead to be transported from Weardale to South Shields on the Tyne. The Crawleyside and Weatherhill inclines, by means of which the line forged its way from Weardale to Parkhead, are today monuments to the audacity of the early railway engineers. From Parkhead a branch line was built in 1846 by the Weardale Iron Company round Bolts Law to Rookhope and Weardale. The summit of the Rookhope incline was 1,670 feet above sea level and the highest point reached by rail in England.

Meanwhile by June 1836, enough of the Newcastle and Carlisle Railway had been built to enable traffic to run from Haydon Bridge to Blaydon. Additional facilities were provided at Haydon Bridge to cater for the lead trade. In December 1852 the branch line from Haltwhistle to Alston was opened but it was never continued to Nenthead as had been the original intention. Similarly, the line projected from Barnard Castle through Middleton-in-Teesdale to Nenthead and Alston was only partly completed; in May 1868 the Barnard Castle to Middleton branch was opened – the only part of the scheme to reach fruition. Another bold venture was the Wear Valley Extension Railway which – when surveyed in 1844-45 – was planned to run the length of the dale and, by means of a tunnel cut two and a quarter miles through the head of the valley, to reach Nenthead. From Nenthead, the line would run to Alston and over Tindale Fell to Brampton where it joined the Newcastle and Carlisle

Railway. In 1847 the first section of the line – from Wear Valley Junction to Frosterley – was opened; the line was extended to Stanhope in 1862 and the final terminus of the line was opened at Wearhead in 1895. The Allendale Railway, which was projected between Hexham and Allenheads, was only built as far as Catton from where there was a connection to the nearby Allen smelt mill. The line was opened in June, 1868. Most of the lines described in this paragraph have ceased to exist, but their remains are impressive monuments to the boldness and ingenuity of the Victorian railway engineers and to the importance of the mineral traffic they were built to carry.

The Groverake Railway

Above: St Peter's Church and Corn Mill
Below: St Peter's - general view

Settlement

Although there is evidence of prehistoric and Roman settlement within the dales, the principal periods of colonisation were after the Roman occupation.

The better farmland at the foot of the dale was colonised largely during Anglian times and it is here that the successors of the Anglian farmsteads can be found. The characteristics of this type of settlement are first, the irregular pattern of the field walls which contrast with the mathematical precision of the field walls built during the period of parliamentary enclosures; secondly, the size of the farm – over fifty acres – which is large in comparison with the others in the dale; thirdly, the large farmhouse with several farm buildings adjoining which were usually built in the eighteenth or nineteenth century to replace earlier buildings. The earliest nucleated settlements – such as the villages of Stanhope, Alston and Allendale Town – are also found near the foot of the dales and owe their origin to a variety of reasons not necessarily connected with mining. In these old market towns are the medieval parish churches. The upper parts of the dales were principally colonised as a result of the great development of lead mining in the eighteenth and nineteenth centuries. The moorland was enclosed with regular field walls, then smallholdings consisting of a farmstead and about five acres of land were established. These were occupied by the miners who practised farming to earn additional money. By the mid-nineteenth century, because of the shortage of land, cottages were built with gardens instead of smallholdings. Also at this time additional accommodation was added to some of the farmsteads to provide lodgings for the miners.

High up the dales new villages were built by the mining communities such as Allenheads and Carshields, which were built by the Blackett-Beaumont Company, and Nenthead and Garrigill which were built by the

London Lead Company. The housing within these villages gives some indication of the standard of accommodation which was provided for the miners; the many chapels emphasize the importance of non-conformist religions among the mining community; the schools, reading rooms and libraries – mainly built during the first half of the nineteenth century – indicate how enlightened this industrial society was in comparison with other working-class communities.

Religion

During the eighteenth century the influence of the Church of England in the lead dales was not great because the parish churches were usually in the old market towns, far from the new mining centres. The parish church at Allendale Town, for example, was a formidable distance from Coalcleugh

Wesleyan Methodist Chapel, Allendale Town

and Allenheads at a time when transport was difficult. Anglican chapels were established at St Peters and Allenheads in East Allendale and at Ninebanks and Carshield in West Allendale but the physical difficulties of securing the necessary offices of baptism, marriage and burial still remained and this perhaps explains the general ineffectiveness of the church.

Wesley first preached at Blanchland in March 1747, and the following year he participated in a public disputation with the curate of Allendale Town. After a checkered early history, Methodism established itself as the principal religion of the dales and as Featherston, the historian of Weardale, remarked, "they have reclaimed and reformed individuals who were enemies to their families and themselves, as well as a perfect pest and disgrace to the neighbourhood". From the 1820s the Primitive Methodists or *Ranters* preached their doctrines of extreme austerity with increasing success: at Nenthead, a young man who entered the chapel with his hair parted carefully down the middle instead of having a straight fringe across the forehead, was expelled from divine service!

By the late nineteenth century, there was a polarisation of classes around the church, the Wesleyan chapel and the Primitive Methodist chapel; the different status of management, skilled workers and men within the industry was perpetuated within the church. Today, the chapels – as the mines – are mainly in ruins.

Education

Charity schools had existed within the dales throughout the eighteenth century, but these were inadequate to cope with the rising population, despite the support of the mining companies. However, a great change took place in the early nineteenth century, partly as a result of the Sunday School movement but chiefly because of the zeal for popular education of three men – Bishop Barrington, Robert Stagg and Thomas Sopwith. Bishop Barrington, following the success of his school at Bishop Auckland in 1819, planned four new schools for Weardale – at Stanhope, Boltsburn, St John's Chapel and Ireshopeburn. These were also supported by the Beaumont family. In the same year Robert Stagg, the new agent of the London Lead Company, opened schools at Middleton and Nenthead which were available to all children, irrespective of whether their fathers

Plaque on the outside wall of the old school, Carshield
Photograph taken in 2006

were employed by the company. In the late 1840s and the early 1850s Thomas Sopwith opened schools in Allendale at Allenheads, Carshield and Sinderhope. However, education was not just acquired at school: work at the mine, the dressing floor or the mill was not a series of thoughtless and repetitive tasks but involved constant decision making, and within the community there was a tradition of literacy:

"There are books in almost every house; attendance on public worship is the rule, not the exception; and profane language is scarcely ever heard. Here is one parish seven miles long without a public house and without a pauper to put in the workhouse."

[Forster's report to the Newcastle Commission, 1861]

Above: View of St Peter's Mine
Below: Allen Bridge and Catton Railway Station

Chapter Six

Route 1: The Allendales
Suggested Map: OS LANDRANGER 87 AND 92

Itinerary – *Haydon Bridge, Langley, Allendale Town, Allenheads, Killhope, Nenthead, Coalcleugh, Carshield, Whitfield, Haydon Bridge.*

Most of Route One lies within the old Manor of Hexhamshire which was bought by Sir William Blackett in 1694 and which became through marriage the property of the Beaumont family, the present Lords of Allendale.

Haydon Bridge

The Beaumont family had a keen interest in the promotion of the Newcastle and Carlisle Railway because transport costs were by far the largest expense incurred in processing the lead ore. It was through the intervention of this powerful family that the line went to Blaydon – where the company's main warehouse and refinery were situated – instead of crossing the Tyne further upstream. Extra facilities were provided at Haydon Bridge station and when it was opened in 1836 the Beaumont Company expected to save £1,500 p.a. on the cost of transporting the lead from Allendale alone. Today, the station yard is no longer served by the railway but it remains a monument to the village's association with the lead industry.

Driving through Haydon Bridge on the A69 towards Hexham, take the RH turn onto the A686, signposted Alston, Langley etc. This takes you past the Anchor public house, where your journey may well end eventually …

Langley

It is difficult to imagine that the peaceful village of Langley was throughout the nineteenth century an important industrial centre with a colliery, fireclay works and one of the largest smelting mills in the northern Pennines. In 1766 the Commissioners of the Greenwich Hospital decided to increase the revenue from their Alston Moor estates by smelting the duty ore themselves. The site of Langley was chosen for the mill because of the availability of local supplies of both coal and peat for the furnaces and the existence of good communications between the mines of Alston

Langley

Moor in the west and the port of Newcastle in the east. When the mill was built in 1767 the smelt house contained four hearths: three for ore and one for slags. The refinery, which was built a short distance away, had two reverberatory furnaces – one for refining and the other for reducing.

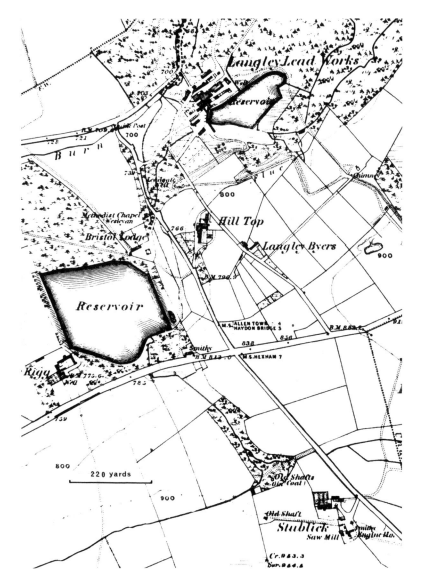

First Edition Ordnance Survey Map of Langley, Published 1865

Langley was an industrial village created by Greenwich Hospital when the lead works was built in 1766. The smelt mill handled both lead and zinc ores. The flue and the reservoirs are marked. The neighbouring Stublick Colliery and the moorland beyond provided coal and peat for the furnaces. The allotments - given to the smelters as an inducement to work at Langley - can be seen near Langley Byers.

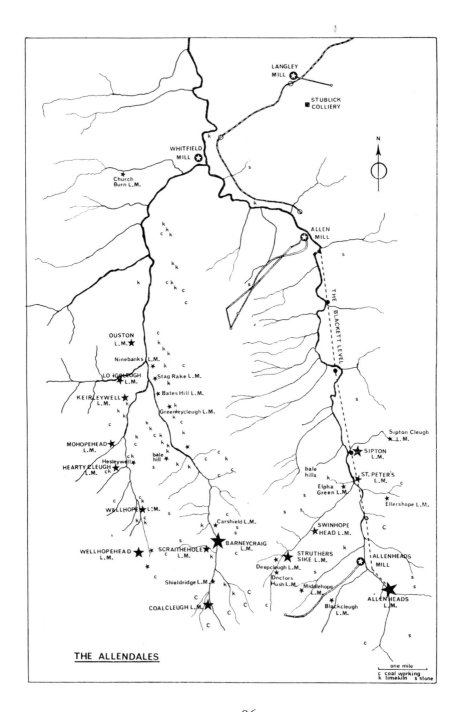

LANGLEY
MILL

STUBLICK
COLLIERY

N

WHITFIELD
MILL

Church
Burn L.M.

ALLEN
MILL

OUSTON
L.M.

Ninebanks L.M.

LO GLEUGH
L.M.

Stag Rake L.M.

KEIRLEYWELL
L.M.

Bates Hill L.M.

Greenleycleugh L.M.

Sipton Cleugh
L.M.

MOHOPEHEAD
L.M.

SIPTON
L.M.

bale
hill

Hesleywell

HEARTYCLEUGH
L.M.

bale
hills

ST. PETER'S
L.M.

Elpha
Green L.M.

Ellershope L.M.

WELLHOPE L.M.

Carshield L.M.

SWINHOPE
HEAD L.M.

WELLHOPEHEAD
L.M.

SCRAITHEHOLE
L.M.

BARNEYCRAIG
L.M.

ALLENHEADS
MILL

STRUTHERS
SIKE L.M.

Deepcleugh L.M.

Shieldridge L.M.

Doctors
Hush L.M.

Middlehope
L.M.

ALLENHEADS
L.M.

COALCLEUGH L.M.

Blackcleugh
L.M.

THE ALLENDALES

THE BLACKETT LEVEL

one mile
c coal working
k limekiln   s stone

There was also the agent's office, the smithy, the lime house, the peat house and the bingsteads. By 1822 three roasting furnaces had been added and there were then seven ore hearths and two refining furnaces in operation. The mill was also smelting zinc. In 1784, another Alston Moor venture, Jobling and Company, was given permission to build a smelt mill and refinery to the north of the Greenwich Hospital works at Langley. Detailed plans exist of both of these smelt mills, dated 1805, which can also be identified on the first edition Ordnance Survey Map, published in 1865. It also shows two large reservoirs fed from the Cragshield level of the neighbouring Stublick Colliery – the water being used to drive two overshot water wheels which powered the mill.

The Greenwich Hospital received constant complaints about the mill reek, the fumes from the furnaces which poisoned the neighbourhood. At first the Commissioners bought thirteen acres of land surrounding the mill and enclosed it with a high wall in an attempt to contain the fumes, but the problem was not solved until the building of the first stage of the long flues between 1801 and 1803. Much of the flue can still be traced up to the site of the Stokoe's condenser and beyond to the large chimney built after 1861, which is a prominent landmark.

To explore the flue at close quarters, drive past the Catton turn off on the road to Hexham from Langley; in about half a mile you will see this exceptionally well-preserved flue chimney on your right, as well as a section of the flue itself. There is plenty of room to park at the side of the road. Return to the Catton turn off.

The road to Catton passes Stublick where a set of early nineteenth century colliery buildings survive, including the engine houses and chimneys for the pumping and winding machinery. Stublick gives its name to a major geological fault which threw the coal measures near the surface and enabled the colliery to supply Langley Mill with coal.

Continue on the B6295 towards Catton, Allendale etc. As you descend towards the village, look ahead and see the twin flue chimneys of the old Alston Mill on the skyline.

Catton

At Catton, take a RH fork down towards the river, signposted B6305 Carrshield, Nenthead.

On your left after the bridge across the East Allen was another old smelt mill, now home to the Allendale Brewery, a local real ale enterprise. The Allen Mill was established in the seventeenth century by the Bacon family of Broadwood Hall and was acquired by the Blacketts in the early eighteenth century. In 1795 a refinery was added and by 1810 over seven thousand ounces of fine silver were being produced annually. In 1821 the mill had two roasting furnaces, five ore hearths, two refining furnaces and one reducing hearth. During the 1850s, the Beaumonts established a library at the mill and the neighbouring school at Brideshill had been used by the workers' children since 1692. The complicated series of flues – one 4,451 yards in length, the other 4,338 yards – wind for a total distance of almost five miles up the hillside.

With the coming of the railway to Catton in 1869 transport problems were eased – a connecting line was built between the station (now a caravan park) and the smelt mill. When the Allendale lead mines finally closed in 1896 the mill ceased to operate.

Back across the bridge there is a pleasant walk to your right along the east bank of the river towards Allendale town, to the entrance to the Blackett Level (see p. 38) which was designed to run the length of the valley to the

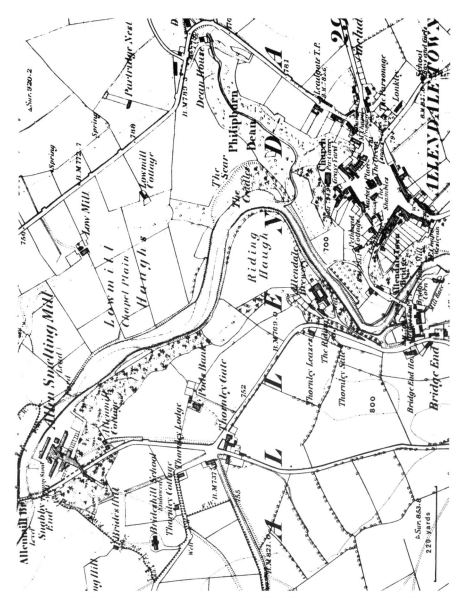

First Edition Ordnance Survey Map of Allendale Town, Published in 1859
The village consists of a cluster of buildings around the market square. Beside the parish church of St Cuthbert both the Primitive and Wesleyan Chapels are marked, and a Quaker Meeting House near Bridgend. The Blackett level entrance is not marked. The smelt mill is situated at a discreet distance from the town.

Gin Hill Shaft at Allenheads mine. Work began in 1855 with the sinking of the shafts at Studdon Dene, Holmes Linn, Sipton and Breckon Hill: the adit was started in 1859 but after intermittent progress the work was abandoned in 1912 when only 4½ miles had been completed. During the half century after the level was projected, the lead trade collapsed and it remains today a sad but impressive monument to the unrealised dreams of the mid Victorian mining industry.

However, the venture was not a complete failure because during the driving of the level three veins were discovered: Esp's vein, Sipton vein and St Peter's vein. They were not brought into production until 1912; the first two veins were worked from Sipton mine, the third from St Peter's mine. The ore from both mines was dressed at Sipton until they were abandoned during the Second World War.

Allendale Town and Allenheads

Continue back over the bridge, past the brewery, up the hill towards Allendale town. Allendale Town is a traditional village clustered around a market square and the parish church and is quite different from the dispersed settlements higher up the dale in the mining districts.

From Allendale Town follow the B6295 to Allenheads. Before you get to Sparty Lea you cross over Sipton Burn (NY 848499). To the right you will see the site of the Sipton mine.

The village of Allenheads consists principally of the mine, the dressing floors, the workshops and amenities like the school, the pub and the church. The miners lived not in the village but in scattered cottages surrounded by smallholdings of about five acres, land which was hard won from the

The Sipton Mine

moorland; as mentioned in Chapter One, farming was always an important adjunct to mining. It was encouraged by the mine owners because it tied the miner to the mine, it provided employment for the womenfolk and enabled them to supplement the family income, and it resulted in land being cultivated which would otherwise have been left as waste. Normally, land over 700 feet is not cultivated in Britain: Allenheads is 1,327 feet above sea level and most of the cottages are at higher altitudes. Now that mining has ceased, the cottages are in other hands and the moorland is again encroaching upon the intake fields.

St Peter's Shaft, Sparty Lea

Allenheads

Allenheads mine was the largest single mine in the northern orefield and produced approximately 260,000 tons of lead concentrates between 1729 and 1896, the period for which records exist. The early workings, which probably belong to the sixteenth and seventeenth centuries, are to the west of the village and are marked by a series of old whimsy shafts. The principal development took place during the eighteenth century when the Gin Hill shaft was sunk below the Great Limestone and the Haugh level, (which had been started a mile to the north in 1694) reached the Gin Hill shaft and acted as the principal drainage level for the mine. In 1776 work began on the Fawside level which was to become the main entrance to the mine in the next century. The Diana vein was discovered in 1792 but was not developed until 1806 when a rich belt of flats was found.

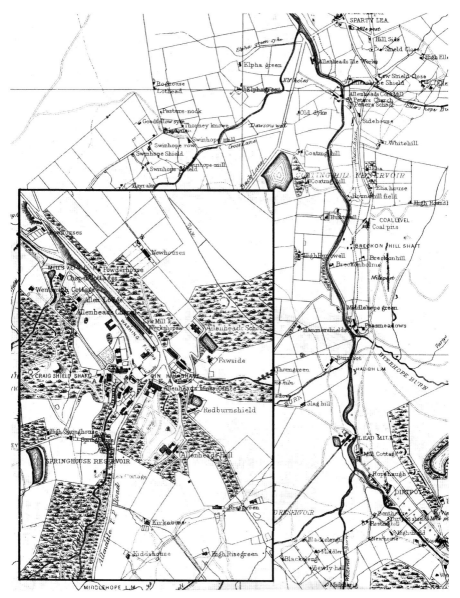

Estate Plan of Allenheads (inset) and the Upper East Allen Valley
Allenheads was a mining centre - the village consisted essentially of the mine, the dressing floors and the workshops. The mining community was dispersed in the scattered cottages at the head of the Dale, each one being surrounded by about five acres of land.

93

Early in the nineteenth century work was in progress with four crosscuts designed to explore the ground to the south. In 1822 the Coronation vein was discovered in the Allercleugh crosscut which proved to be exceptionally rich and yielded 7.163 tons of lead concentrates between 1824 and 1840, by which time it was almost exhausted. Henry's vein had been found in 1796 during the driving of the Fawside level but it was not developed until after 1825 and it became the mainstay of the mine during the later part of its life.

An amazing series of reservoirs with a total capacity of over sixty million gallons supplied the power for the mine, the dressing floors and the smelt mill. Although water power had been used earlier, the system that is visible today was largely the work of Thomas Sopwith, the friend of William Armstrong. Armstrong, the founder of the famous Elswick factory on Tyneside, had first achieved success as an hydraulics engineer and one of his engines is on display at the Allenheads Heritage Centre. Water from the Corbitmea dam in the Rookhope valley was led down the Corbitmea shaft and along the Fawside level in pipes to two underground engines which discharged into the Fawside level. This water together with water from the surface engines and other sources, after being used on the dressing floors, was conducted by a shallow adit back into the mine. The stream was used to drive four underground wheels placed in sequence at different levels in different shafts below Allenheads village. The engines were used for pumping water up to the Haugh level which also drained the tail-water away into the East Allen at Peasmeadow. The waste water from the Allenheads smelt mill, which was supplied from the Dodd and Smelt mill reservoirs, also drained into the East Allen. Eight water wheels, two at each of the shafts on the Blackett level, and four corn mills were powered by the same water before it was again diverted, this time to drive the machinery at the Allen smelt mill beyond Allendale Town.

The smelt mill at Allenheads was built by the Blacketts in the early eighteenth century and by 1821 there were three ore hearths, one roasting furnace and one slag hearth in operation. The carrier's way by which the Weardale ores were brought across Killhope to the smelt mill and, on the eastern side of the valley the route of the Galloway ponies across the fells to the refinery at Dukesfield and the warehouses at Blaydon, can still be traced. The flue of the smelt mill is 3,424 feet in length and this, together with a row of deserted cottages, a water wheel and the overgrown reservoir is all that now remains of the mill which closed in 1870. The neighbourhood has the unattractive but significant name of Dirt Pot, as shown on the estate plan of 1861 and clearly marked on today's OS map. The scattered nature of Allenheads village, dominated by the mine in the centre and Allenheads Hall (built for Thomas Sopwith), can also be seen.

The main road south from Allenheads passes the site of the great Burtree Pasture mine near Cowshill which was bought by the Blacketts in 1791 and became their most productive mine in Weardale. It is an interesting run down the dale to Ireshopeburn and High House Chapel, now the oldest chapel in the world to have been in continuous use. Do take the time to visit the chapel and small museum; there is a beautiful recreation of a typical miner's family living room and considerable information about the lead mining era, including 'what happened next' – when the mines closed. The adjacent Weardale Inn was first built as a school for miners' children. Across the valley is Newhouse – an impressive home built for the chief agent of the Beaumont Company in Weardale; Thomas Sopwith installed a reading room for the miners in the little hamlet which developed around this big house.

After visiting Ireshopeburn, turn back up the road, through Wearhead, and take the A689 in the direction of Alston.

Killhope Lead Mining Museum

At the head of Weardale is the award winning Killhope Lead Mining Museum which is one of the most instructive sites to visit relating to the former lead mining industry. The massive water wheel at Killhope is a striking feature on the landscape; built at Armstrong's factory in Newcastle, it drove the machinery on the dressing floor. The complex known as Park Level Mill was built by the Beaumont Company between 1876 and 1878 to replace an earlier crushing mill at Burn Bottom, further west. Park Level had been started in 1853 as a crosscut, driven westwards to intersect the known veins at the head of the valley which were being worked from the surface. After twenty years of driving this level, rich mineral deposits were found which lead to the decision to build the new mill. The mine and the mill operated until 1916. In the 1920s the mill was robbed of its machinery to supply parts for other mines; the jigs, for example, were sent to Boltsburn. The site remained derelict until 1968, when Durham County Council began the development which has resulted in the impressive museum that you see today.

Water still flows from the entrance of Park Level – the entrance to the mine. As with other levels in the area it is beautifully lined with dry stone work. Organised tours into the level and mine workings are one of the features of a visit to this museum. Next to the mine entrance is a building housing the stables and the smithy, above which are the agent's office and the mine shop, both of which have been restored to give an excellent impression of mining life in the late nineteenth century.

A light railway ran from the mine to the bouse teems where the undressed ore from the different veins was dumped. Water was used to clean the bouse and the obvious lumps of galena and stone were hand picked from the mass: the galena was sent to the bingstead, the stones to the waste heap. All the mixture which could not be separated by hand was put into a wagon and hauled up the incline to the crusher by a power take off from the great wheel. The mixture was tipped into a hopper which fed the crushing rollers. Next it was made to pass over a set of trammels which graded the mixture: the smallest, less than ¼ inch, went directly to the buddle house; the largest, more than ¾ inch, was returned to the crushers; the remainder was fed to the four jiggers which were mechanically operated. The lower building housed the buddles which were powered by a small waterwheel. The waste from all of the operations was collected in settling tanks where the last attempt at separation was made.

A constant supply of water was essential not only to power the water wheels but for every aspect of the dressing process. A race beginning at Cobblers Level high up the Killhope Burn supplied the large overshot water wheel while another race beginning at Cowhorse Hush supplied the buddlehouse and lower dressing floors. Four dams on the hillside above the mill collected the water from another two races which was used as a reserve supply. The ore was not smelted at Killhope, but was instead taken to Allenheads and, after the closure of this smelt mill in 1870, was taken either to the Allen smelt mill or to Rookhope. The musem has a very good display of the minerals found in the area, including a collection of spar boxes – a good introduction to the geology of the region.

The road to Killhope Cross passes the deserted farmsteads of upper Weardale, once the highest and loneliest cottages in England. Old *hushes* scar the sides of the hills. Beyond the summit is the Nent valley, the most productive part of the Alston Moor orefield, from which three quarters of the total lead produced on Alston Moor has been mined. From the fort at Whitley Castle, near Alston, the Romans sought the surface veins of the orefield which, in medieval times supplied the Carlisle mint with silver. However, it was during the eighteenth century that the major developments took place under the direction of the Greenwich Hospital for Seamen which in 1735 had acquired practically the entire moor as part of the confiscated estates of the Derwentwater family, the local leaders of the 1715 Jacobite rebellion.

In 1739 only 360 tons were produced, but by 1765 the figure was 6,000 tons and in 1825 a peak of 7,200 tons was recorded. The Commissioners, who leased the mineral rights in return for a duty (usually of 20% of the ore produced), resisted the attempts of the London Lead Company to establish a monopoly of the leases by encouraging small groups of adventurers. Nonetheless, although the Quaker Company always held less than 50% of the leases and never enjoyed the dominance that the Beaumonts did in Weardale, it was the largest and most influential concern.

Nenthead

By 1745 the London Lead Company held the leases of the large Priorsdale estate and several of the mines around Nenthead. The company had also bought the Nenthead smelt mill from George Liddell of Ravensworth, which it remodelled and which began production in August, 1746. In the next decade they promoted the development of the village by building cottages near to the smelt mill and beside the Gillgill Burn for the smelters and officials, while they encouraged the development of farmsteads to house the miners. During the 1820s a new village was built which included a school, a market hall, a chapel and thirty-five cottages. Today, Hillersdon Terrace, built as the new accommodation for the officials and the smelters, still stands as a monument to the company's welfare policy and a contradiction to many of the generalisations customarily made about the early industrial revolution.

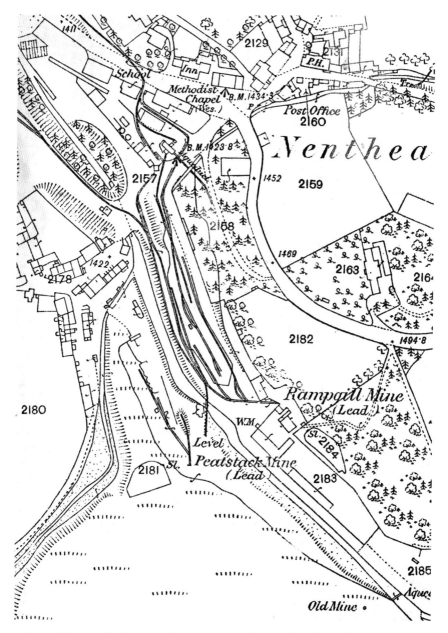

First Edition Ordnance Survey Map of Nenthead, Published 1858
Scale: 25 inches to 1 mile

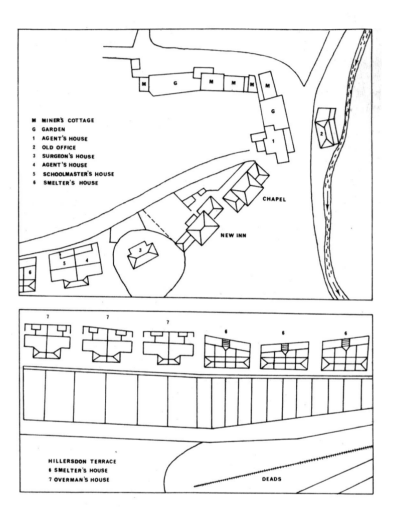

M MINER'S COTTAGE
G GARDEN
1 AGENT'S HOUSE
2 OLD OFFICE
3 SURGEON'S HOUSE
4 AGENT'S HOUSE
5 SCHOOLMASTER'S HOUSE
6 SMELTER'S HOUSE

CHAPEL

NEW INN

HILLERSDON TERRACE
6 SMELTER'S HOUSE
7 OVERMAN'S HOUSE

DEADS

Estate plan of Nenthead

At about this time the washing floors and the smelt mill were re-organised and the long flue can still be traced to the weathered chimney. The company continued its policy of developing farmsteads and beginning plantations, especially after the enclosure of Alston Moor and Priorsdale in 1815.

About 1865 the cottages beside the Gillgill Burn were rebuilt and a new school, a bath-house and public wash-house were added to the village. In 1882 the London Lead Company sold their interests in the Alston Moor estate to Cameron Swan and Company of Newcastle who subsequently resold it to the Belgian firm, Vieille Montagne Zinc. Despite the addition of council houses and the recent attempts to beautify the village, Nenthead remains substantially the creation of the Quaker Company.

The Commissioners of the Greenwich Hospital always held a deep interest in their estate. They employed John Smeaton the builder of the Eddystone lighthouse, to drive the Nentforce level in 1776. This drained and explored the whole valley for 4½ miles below Nenthead. The mining companies were encouraged to build horse levels and during the late eighteenth and early nineteenth centuries a remarkable network of underground communications developed linking many of the Nenthead mines, not only with each other but also with the Beaumont mines in West Allendale. This network enabled the ore to be dressed at central points instead of at the individual mines which was the old practice. At Nenthead, the dressing floor at Smallcleugh handled the ore from the Smallcleugh level which was over four miles in length and led to the veins at the head of the valley; the larger dressing floors at Rampgill were re-organised in 1818 to deal with the ores from the Rampgill and Caplecleugh levels, both almost four miles in length.

The effects of the depression in the lead industry at the end of the nineteenth century were offset by the demands for zinc, which was plentiful in the Nenthead area. The *Vieille Montagne Zinc Company* re-opened many of the old lead mines of the Nent valley and West Allendale for blende and made full use of the underground communications. In 1908 the Belgian firm built a large gravity mill on the site of the old low Rampgill dressing floor which was a five storey building capable of handling 200 tons of blende in a twelve hour shift. The mill was closed in 1921 but re-opened in part after the sinking of the Wellhope shaft in 1925 to which it was connected by aerial ropeway. Between the wars the principal development was at the Nentsberry mine when an important set of veins at Wellhopehead were opened up from the Nentsberry Horse level. The bouse was treated at the Nentsberry mill. During the Second World War, a flotation plant capable of dressing 1,000 tons of gravel from the old spoil heaps each day was housed in the old Nenthead mill. Today its shell is used as a garage.

The Vieille Montagne Zinc Company used compressed air not only for ventilation but for pumping, hoisting and drilling. The compressed air plant was supplied by three reservoirs: Perry dam with a capacity of 16,500,000 gallons, Smallcleugh dam with a capacity of 375,000 gallons and Coalcleugh dam in West Allendale with a capacity of 2,500,000 gallons. Water from Perry dam was taken in pipes to Bogg shaft where air was admitted into the descending pipes. The falling water drew the air into a bell shaped receiver and the water escaped through an ascending pipe to a height of about 200 feet. This column of water provided the pressure necessary to compress the air to about 90lb per square inch. The overflow was used to supply the Smallcleugh dam which supplied a similar system in the Brewery shaft. The Coalcleugh dam supplied the Barney Craig shaft.

In the post war period, mining struggled on until activities finally ceased in 1965. The site remained derelict until the North Pennines Heritage Trust was formed in 1987, which promoted the development of Nenthead Mines as a tourist attraction and as a centre for research into industrial archaeology. The Nenthead Mines cover a vast site and claim to be the largest lead mining complex in Britain.

The road up the Nent Valley from Nenthead leads to the Entrance and Visitors' Centre, where an exhibition tells the story of Nenthead. Continuing up the valley there is an interesting display demonstrating the power of water – so important to the mining industry. Overshot and undershot water wheels have been reconstructed, and they provide electricity for the site. Next is the smelt mill, built in 1737 and closed in 1896. The assay house, where the assayer once worked assessing samples from the mines, survives with its tall chimney; it is believed to be the last remaining assay house in the country. The climax of the visit is to enter the mine itself, which one does via the horse level built by the London Lead Company in 1815. This level leads to Carr's vein, where working practices such as *stopes* and *flats* can be seen. Peter Wilkinson, who helped to develop my interest in lead mining, is largely responsible for this fascinating educational experience. The hillsides are scarred with other sites which can be visited, including Smallcleugh reservoir, the big wheel pit and the Brewery shaft at the head of the Nent Level.

Nenthall

Mid-way between Nenthead and Alston is Nenthall, once the home of mine owner John Wilson, now a hotel. Here one can enjoy a meal in the former residence of the man who 'hit the jackpot' with the discovery of rich veins in the Hudgill Burn mine – hence the wealth to build this impressive mansion.

Alston

The Nent Level began 4½ miles away near Alston railway station. The line to Haltwhistle, once so important to the mining industry, has closed. However, Alston station and the line at the head of the valley has re-opened as a narrow gauge steam railway. Alston prides itself as being the highest market town in England, and is an attractive village to visit.

Coalcleugh

Returning to Nenthead along the A689, the road to the West Allen valley is signposted Carrshield and Allenheads. It follows roughly the line of the Scaleburn and the Coalcleugh veins and, on the approach to the almost deserted village of Coalcleugh, the rake representing the earliest workings of the Coalcleugh mine can be seen on the left-hand side. Coalcleugh level was started in 1789 and ultimately led to the Coalcleugh, Whitewood and Barneycraig veins. The mine has a place in history as the site where Westgarth Forster developed the first underground hydraulic engine in 1765. Although Coalcleugh is 1,750 feet above sea level, farmsteads were worked by the old lead miners. Today these are in ruins, or have been converted into holiday homes.

Carrshield (also written Carshield)

The main mining centre was at Carrshield a mile to the north at a modest 1,300 feet. It was here that the Barneycraig level was begun in 1760 although the vein was not reached until the early nineteenth century. The dried up reservoirs which supplied the main dressing floors, the smithy and the miners' shop still survive albeit in a ruined state; the school, the chapels, the agents house and the miners' cottages are mainly used by weekend visitors.

The ore from West Allendale was smelted at the Allen mill and it was taken across the moorland by the carrier's way from Coalcleugh or by the lead road from Carrshield.

Taking a LH downhill turn towards Whitfield, the low road from Carrshield leads to the Hexham-Penrith road, a turnpike road improved by John McAdam for the Greenwich Hospital in the 1820s. By 1829 the

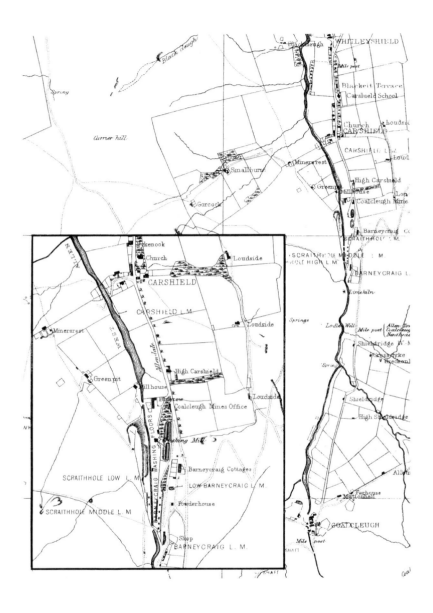

Estate Plan of Carshield (inset) and the Upper East Allen Valley, 1861
Again, the dispersed nature of the mining settlements is clearly shown.

Commissioners were saving £250 p.a. on the carriage of duty ore from the Alston Moor mines to Langley mill. Nothing now remains of the much older mill at the delightful village of Whitfield except a barn by the side of the road which may have been a peat store, and the place name evidence of 'cupola' at the confluence of the East and West Allen (see map).

In 1706 the London Lead Company leased the old mill at Whitfield which the company preferred to the Ryton mill because of the savings in transport costs. The mill both smelted and refined lead ores from Alston Moor for more than a century using coal from the Coanwood district of the South Tyne. However, as a result of the re-organisation of the industry at Nenthead in the early nineteenth century, the mill was closed in 1816 and by 1821 was in ruins.

The road back to Haydon Bridge passes through the beautiful West Allen valley, winds its way up Staward Peel past the old railway station at Staward and on to Langley Mill and castle. On returning to Haydon Bridge, enjoy a drink at the Anchor, so called because an anchor was the symbol of the Greenwich Hospital for Seamen, a major force in the Lead Mining history of the area.

Chapter Seven

Route 2: The Derwent Mines, the Rookhope Valley and Stanhopeburn

Suggested Maps: OS LANDRANGER 87 AND 92

Itinerary: *Hexham, Blanchland, Hunstanworth, Rookhope, Stanhope, Crawleyside and return to Hexham.*

Route two passes through some of the north's most beautiful countryside, an area which was alive with industrial activity in the nineteenth century. Today the lead mining and silver production have ceased, the ironstone and limestone quarries have stopped working and a large proportion of the population has deserted the dales. Nonetheless, the scars remain as an archaeological record of a bygone society.

Take the B6306 (Eastgate) from Hexham towards Slaley, which leaves Hexham's main thoroughfare between Pattinsons Chemist and the Tap and Spile Public House. As you climb out of Hexham, ignore the right hand fork to Slaley for commercial vehicles. At Linnels Bridge, the road from Hexham crosses the Devil's Water which is romantically associated with Dorothy Forster, the Derwentwater family and the abortive Jacobite rebellion of 1715.

Follow the signs to Whitley Chapel.

The small mines further up the valley are insignificant in mining history, but there was a large smelt mill at Dukesfield, once an important centre for the production of both lead and silver. It was built during the early eighteenth century to handle the ores from the Beaumont mines in Allendale and Weardale. The carriers' ways, gouged out of the moorland by the tramping of the Galloway ponies, can still be traced across the hills from the mines to the smelt mill, and the minor roads eastwards originated as carriers' ways to the large refinery and warehouses of the Blackett-Beaumont Company at Blaydon.

With the increased demand for silver, refining furnaces were added in the 1770s and by the 1790s silver production had reached a peak of over 8,000 ounces per annum. However, silver production ceased at Dukesfield in about 1805 when a refinery was built at the Allen Mill, although the Weardale ores continued to be smelted until the mill closed in 1834. The buildings were demolished in 1837 but part of the flue survives as an isolated pair of gothic arches, which may be found in the woodland by the side of Devils Water, (NY 941579).

At the roadbridge over the Devil's Water there is a layby on the left and a footpath signposted into the wood. Follow this path for about 300 yards and the arches are found on the left hand side.

These arches are a stirring reminder of a passed time, when architectural beauty mattered even in lead smelting.

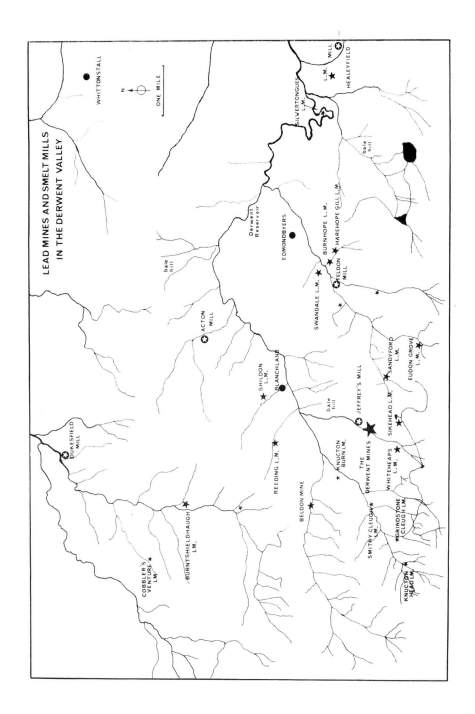

Make your way back to the B6306, and follow it towards Blanchland.

Acton Mills

Beyond Slaley Forest the road descends to open moorland, purple with heather in late summer. It crosses the Acton Burn (NY 982 534). The burn was at one time a small tributary of the River Derwent, but it now flows into the Derwent Reservoir. The burn was the site of two smelt mills. High Acton Mill was in existence in the early seventeenth century and is sometimes referred to as Shildon Mill because it handled ore from the neighbouring mine at Shildon. Low Acton Mill was built by the London Lead Company in about 1745, presumably to deal with the increased output from their mines in the Derwent Valley. For a time in the 1760s, ore from Fallowfield north of the Tyne was smelted here and it would have been transported along the road taken from Hexham. The mills were linked by carriers' ways to the Shildon mine and more distant Nent Valley mines of the London Lead Company. Ores from these mines were smelted and refined at Acton until 1808, when the Quaker company lost its leases in the Derwent Valley for failing to maintain the mines properly. The mills were abandoned in the early nineteenth century.

Blanchland and Shildon Mine

Blanchland is a settlement which was founded amongst the wild and isolated Northumberland moors in 1165 for an order of Augustinian monks, the Premonstratensian Canons, also known as 'White' Monks because of their pale robes. Today it is a picturesque village swamped by tourists who clamour for a glimpse of Dorothy Forster's ghost – and more mundane pleasures – in the Lord Crewe Arms, once the Abbot's guest house.

The village was remodelled in the eighteenth century by the Crewe estate but it retains the plan of a monastic establishment. It is a sober reflection on the popular taste for history that the hint of the supernatural among pseudo-medieval surroundings attracts great attention while at the Shildon mine, just a short distance away, the crumbling ruins of the only remaining Cornish engine house in the north are unnoticed. Probably the oldest mine in the district, Shildon is mentioned in a grant of Edward IV dated 1475 – although it was not worked on a large scale until the eighteenth century. This mine, in common with others in the area, was noted for the high content of silver in the lead ore. It is approached from the path leading northwards from the old school (now a café) past the car park; the village is on the right, the engine house on the left and the vein across the road.

Leave Blanchland on the road to Stanhope, towards the south west.

The principal mines of the Derwent Company lie further west, past the sprawling village of Hunstanworth, in the Boltsburn valley. In 1690, Jeffrey's Rake was leased by William Forster of Bamburgh to Thomas Rawlins of Durham and in 1708, the London Lead Company took over the lease and began in addition the development of the Whiteheaps and Ramshaw mines. A new mill was built at Jeffrey's in 1713 to serve the Derwent mines which were extensively developed during the eighteenth century. However, in 1805 the Trustees of the Lord Crewe estates refused to renew the leases and later prosecuted the London Lead Company for neglect of the mines. Subsequently the lease was taken up by a local syndicate, *Easterby, Hall and Company,* owners of a red lead mill in Newcastle. The new company embarked upon an ambitious programme of development which included the installation of steam engines and exploration into the Great Limestone. This soon resulted in its financial collapse and in 1812 the mines were taken over by the principal creditors, who formed the Derwent Mining

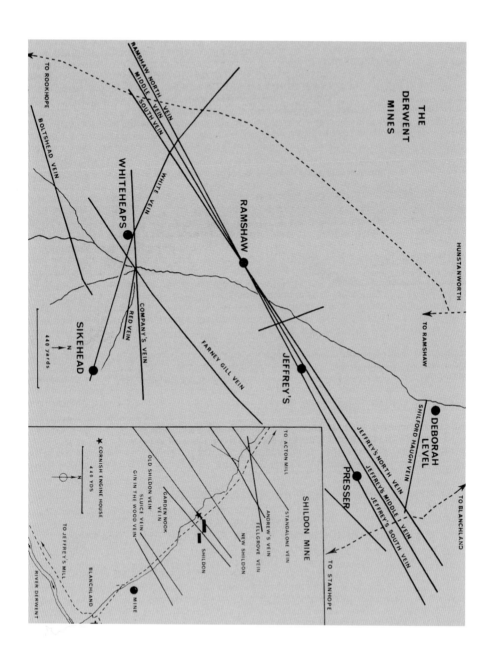

Company. Except at Shildon – where the Cornish engine house can still be seen standing on the old Shildon vein – the new company replaced the steam engines with hydraulic power. In about 1820, the Boulton and Watt engine at Shildon was sold to Backworth colliery near Newcastle, and the engine house was converted into accommodation for miners. It became known locally as 'Shildon Castle'.

Travelling westward from Blanchland to Baybridge, the road swings south across the river, past Balehill House on your right, after which a road on the right leads to Ramshaw, signposted Hunstanworth, Townsfield. At Ramshaw were concentrated most of the dressing floors and smelt mills. With the help of the first edition O.S. map it is possible to explore the remains. In Ramshaw hamlet you can see some interesting features; most of the larger buildings have been converted into homes.

The network of aqueducts and dams can still be explored: indeed, some of the system is today being used by the local water board which, since the 1920s, has also pumped water from the Jeffrey and Ramshaw veins at a station on the site of the old Presser mine. MacKenzie records that in 1825 the ..

> *"whole body of water available is made to pass over and supply, first a pressure engine at Whiteheaps, next a water wheel 44 feet in diameter at Ramshaw and afterwards a water wheel 48 feet in diameter at Jeffreys; all pumping, besides going over and supplying several wheels for the crushing mills and smelting mills."*

This description can only refer to part of the existing remains, namely those associated with the Burnhead and Whiteheaps dams. The much more extensive collection system associated principally with the Sikehead and Burnhope dams – clearly indicated on the first edition of the Ordnance

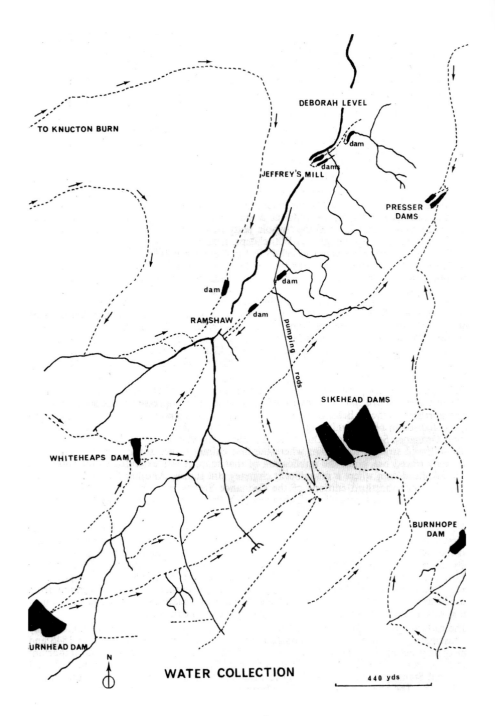

TO KNUCTON BURN

DEBORAH LEVEL

dam

JEFFREY'S MILL

dams

PRESSER DAMS

dam

dam

RAMSHAW

dam

pumping rods

SIKEHEAD DAMS

WHITEHEAPS DAM

BURNHOPE DAM

URNHEAD DAM

N

WATER COLLECTION

440 yds

Survey map (1857) – is an archaeological record of the mid-nineteenth century prosperity of the Derwent mines. The census returns of the period speak volumes: the population rose from 430 in 1801, to 995 in 1831, to a peak of 1,233 in 1861. The statistical returns show that during the period 1845 to 1883 the output of lead ore was 39,409 tons; and during the period 1853 to 1883 the production of silver was 220,383 ounces.

Jeffrey's Mill

Nowadays only scant remains of the smelt mill and refinery can be seen at Jeffrey's Mill on the banks of the Boltsburn, but the network of flues is the most impressive to be seen anywhere in the northern orefield. Behind the site of Jeffrey's Mill a maze of subterranean passage-ways, collapsed in places, only vaguely resembles what is inadequately marked on the first edition Ordnance Survey map. On the south side of the vein complex the twin flue can be easily followed straight to the point where the first chimney once stood. **To see this, follow the dead end towards Boltshope Farm; there is a footpath over to the flues and chimneys.** The branch flue is also easily traced but, since the publication of that map, it was extended to the south end of the Sikehead dam where a magnificent chimney still stands. **Directions to visit this chimney via an easier walk are found later in this route.** Another flue, shown neither on the first nor the third editions of the Ordnance Survey map (surely an error) can be followed from the recently collapsed chimney to the roadway from which it presumably went directly to the mill.

An interesting network of wagonways is shown on the first edition of the Ordnance Survey map. The gravity inclines leading from the Presser mine down to the dressing plant near the Deborah level and from the Sikehead mine to the dressing floor at Whiteheaps can easily be traced. The wagonway connecting Whiteheaps with Jeffrey's Mill and the Deborah is difficult to find because of the overgrowth. In the 1860s, the Derwent mines were linked to the Weardale Iron Company's system by a branch railway line running from Dead Friar's to Sikehead and the self acting incline was replaced by a haulage engine now that it was necessary to transport the loaded wagons up the incline.

The railway system built in the mid-nineteenth century by the Weardale Iron Company is a fascinating study in itself. The company was formed by Charles Attwood in 1846 and immediate action was taken to connect the furnaces at Tow Law with the important sources of ironstone and limestone in upper Weardale. A branch was built from Parkhead on the old Stanhope and Tyne Railway to Middlehope and the large ironstone quarries at Slitt Pasture. The line climbed 1,670 feet above sea level at Bolt's Law (the highest altitude attained by railways in England) where it dropped by an incline of 1:12 to Rookhope. The remains of the engine house, the locomotive shed and a row of railway cottages are now considerably dilapidated. The line was extended south to Smailsburn and by means of another incline up to Middlehope and the important Slitt Pasture ironstone mines in Weardale. In the 1860s a branch was built from Rookhope, past Lintzgarth smelter, past the mines at Rispey, Wolfcleugh and Groverake to the ironstone deposits at the head of the Rookhope valley. The quarries at Frazer's Hush and Northgrain were worked until 1877 but the lead mines continued to be served by the railway until 1923 and supplies for Boltsburn were hauled by horses along the Parkhead line until the railway was finally closed in about 1940.

Directions to Rookhope:

From Ramshaw the road climbs out of the valley to Townfield, overlooking the village of Hunstanworth. This settlement was built in 1863 by the Reverend Daniel Capper, to cope with the rising population caused by the success of the mines on his estate. Turning left, the moorland road leads to Rookhope. As you travel up the road you can clearly see on your left the chimneys of Jeffrey's Mill, across the valley. To the right on a clear day there are spectacular views from the summit across Northumberland to the distant Cheviot Hills – a reminder of why this county is known as 'the land of far horizons'. The road drops dramatically down Rimey Law into the Rookhope valley at Redburn. This was the site of an important mine, and also of the Rookhope borehole which was driven in 1960-61 through the strata to prove the existence of Weardale granite 427 yards (390.5 metres) beneath.

The Weardale mines were owned by the Dean and Chapter of Durham and there are several references to both lead and iron mining during medieval times. Between 1698 and 1882 the majority of the mines were leased to the Blackett-Beaumont Company which was responsible for

The ruins of the water-wheel at Rookhope

the large scale development of lead mining in upper Weardale. This company built the smelter at Lintzgarth in 1737 to replace an earlier near Rookhope.

There was no refinery at Lintzgarth and the lead was sent to Dukesfield or Blaydon for silver extraction. Early in the nineteenth century the long flue was added and the smelter remained in operation until 1919 when it achieved fame as the last of the twenty-eight smelt mills in the northern orefield to be closed. The mines in the upper part of the valley – Rispey, Wolfcleugh and Groverake – were drained by the Tailrace level which is some 9,175 feet in length. Some lead ore was obtained at Rispey but it became important as an iron mine. The Beaumont Company abandoned the mines in the Rookhope valley in 1882 after which date they were leased to the Weardale Lead Company which has survived through intermittent periods of prosperity and recession until recently. This company built the narrow gauge railway from Groverake mine down the valley to Wolfcleugh mine and the dressing floors at Rispey. After the lead had been dressed it was taken by horse and cart to the smelt mill at Lintzgarth less than a mile away.

The single arch which once carried the flue across the road and the ruins of the flue are all that remains of this important smelting site which closed in 1919. **To find this, turn to your right at the bottom of Rimey Law hill. You will find a small car park (once the site of a cleaning tank) and a useful information point. If you continue up the road towards Allenheads for about 3 miles you can see the impressive remains of the Groverake Mine (NY 896441). After the Second World War, fluorspar was produced here by British Steel until it closed in 1985.**

Retrace your route past the arch towards Rookhope.

The most important mine in the valley is the Boltsburn mine at Rookhope (NY 937438), which was developed by the Beaumont Company and taken over by the Weardale Lead Company in 1883. The discovery of extensive flats in the great limestone made Boltsburn the most productive mine in the country during the first decades of the last century. Between 1901 and 1931, 89,370 tons of lead concentrates were produced from the flats. The mine was abandoned in 1940 because of flooding. After the Second World War fluorspar production was also developed by the Weardale Lead Company (part of ICI) at the Redburn mine, which was closed in 1981.

Follow the road towards Stanhope, via Eastgate.
Landranger Map 92

Beyond the mining community of Rookhope is the village of Eastgate, once the entrance to Weardale forest, the hunting grounds of the prince-bishops of Durham. Now the hillsides are bare. By the nineteenth century, the bishops of Durham and the rectors of Stanhope were receiving over £4,000 per annum each from the lead industry as a result of their manorial and ecclesiastical rights over Weardale. This wealth is reflected in the architecture of the village of Stanhope with the bishop's castle built as a country mansion in 1798 dominating the western side of the village square and the rectory, lavishly rebuilt in 1821, commanding the eastern side. A petrified tree stands in the grounds of the medieval village church which houses some fine examples of polished marble from the famous Frosterley quarries.

Of less traditional interest but equally impressive is the industrial archaeology of Crawleyside and the Stanhopeburn valley. The construction of the Stanhope and Tyne Railway between 1832 and 1834 was one of the great achievements of the early railway age. There is no finer monument to the boldness of its engineers – Robert Stephenson and T E Harrison – than the scars of the old Crawleyside and Weatherhill inclines forging their way from the freight depots at Lanehead up and out of Stanhopeburn to the bleak moorland beyond. George Stephenson designed the 50 hp engines which were used on the inclines until 1918: they were built by the famous Gateshead ironmaster, George Hawks. The climb was a steep one with gradients of 1:12 and 1: 8 to Crawleyside and 1:32 and 1:13 to Weatherhill – rising a total of 650 feet in 1 mile, 1,066 yards.

Unfortunately only piles of rubble mark the sites of the engine houses and the odd stone sleeper the line of the track, which was closed in 1951. The original company soon ran into financial difficulty and in 1840 the western half of the railway between Consett and Stanhope was closed. This was re-opened in 1842 by the Derwent Iron Company which was just beginning production at Consett and needed access to the limestone and iron ore of Weardale. The iron company had a close association with the Stockton and Darlington Railway Company which took over the line in 1847. This explains the S & D plaque on the cottages at Weatherhill and the several S & D marker stones along the line.

The track up the Stanhopeburn valley follows the course of the old railway to the lead mines, the ironstone workings and the limestone quarries. The Stanhopeburn mine dates to at least the eighteenth century when it was worked by the Earl of Carlisle and Company which probably smelted the ore at the old mill, high up in the valley. At the beginning of the nineteenth century the London Lead Company extended the Shield Hurst level and worked the Red Vein until 1854. The Quaker Company also built the Stanhope mill with a reverberatory furnace and a horizontal flue which today is a ruin. The London Lead Company relinquished their leases in 1854 but lead mining continued under the Beaumont Company between 1866 and 1875. In 1906, the Weardale Lead

Company re-opened the mine for fluorspar and Stanhopeburn became the leading spar mine in the district. The company ceased operations in 1933 but mining continued intermittently on a small scale until recently.

Crawleyside

At Crawleyside the vein was worked as an open cut for spar by the Weardale Iron Company from 1854 while the Beaumont Company drove the Hope level from the east bank of the burn between 1868 and 1877 in an unsuccessful attempt to find wageable deposits of lead ore. In 1914 the level was re-opened for spar. Extensive deposits of iron are associated with the Red vein in Stanhopeburn as in the neighbouring Rookhope valley.

These have been mined at Noah's Ark quarry by open cut mining and at Red Vein quarry from the level. The Stanhopeburn iron works was established by Cuthbert Rippon in 1845 but had only a brief existence before it was superseded by Tow Law.

The Great Limestone has been extensively quarried on the east side of the valley. Lanehead quarry was in operation when the railway was opened in 1834 and production was expanded as the iron industry developed in the north-east. By the 1850s, 150,000 tons of limestone were being produced and seventeen kilns were in operation. This quarry was exhausted by the end of the nineteenth century and Ashes quarry, which had been started on a small scale in the 1870s, was developed by the Consett Iron Company after 1901. About this time the Lanehead kilns stopped working. In the 1920s, two hundred men were employed at Ashes quarry and over 100,000 tons of limestone was sold annually. The quarry had closed by 1949 but four of the old Lanehead kilns, which had been restarted in 1938, were working until the 1960s.

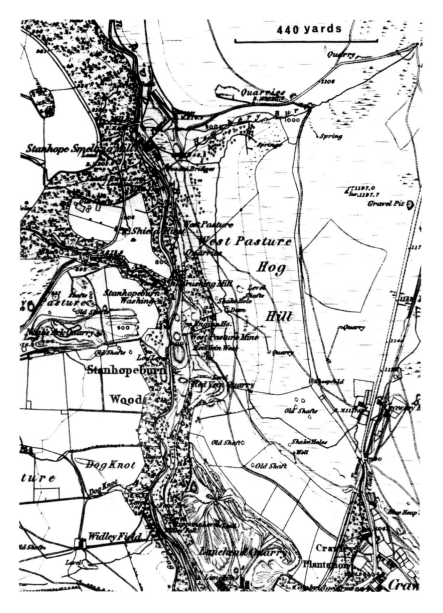

First Edition Ordnance Survey Map of Stanhopeburn, Published in 1861
This pleasant valley was once an important site of lead mining, smelting, iron working and limestone quarrying. Note the terminus of the Stanhope and Tyne railway at the Lanehead Quarry. It had not yet been extended eastwards to Crawleyside.

The road forks at the top of Crawleyside bank: on the left is the direct route back to Blanchland and Hexham. Although the route continues to Healeyfield and Edmundbyers, a short detour will take you to a place where you can walk across the moor to view one of the chimneys that you saw in the distance at Ramshaw:

Continue along the Hexham branch in the road for about three miles to NY 964475. Follow the path over the moors approx. twenty minutes walking. You will also find Sikehead Dam with the reservoir behind it. Leading up to the chimney one can see the line of the collapsed flue running north west into Bolts Burn valley.

Return to the fork in the road and turn sharp left towards **Healeyfield** and the **Edmundbyers** mines. There is a tradition that the Healeyfield mine, (NZ 069487) near Castleside, is ancient and once supplied the Durham mint with silver. Certainly the Dean and Chapter of Durham owned the mine which, judging from the returns made in the late nineteenth century, was especially rich in silver, the ore yielding 15 ounces per ton. The mine was active in 1810 when Bailey conducted his survey of the County of Durham and during the period 1853 to 1891 the statistics indicate an annual production of 188 tons of lead and 3,009 ounces of silver.

By the 1920s the mine was in a ruinous state and the remains of extensive mine plants were visible in Dean Howl. Today little sense can be made of the debris. The ore was smelted at the Healeyfield mill, on the outskirts of Castleside, which was erected in 1805 and continued to smelt lead ore until 1913. Today the unimpressive remains of the twin flues are preserved by Durham County Council.

Further up the valley the small **Silvertongue** mine (NZ 056493) was worked some time between 1828 and 1850 and appears to have been profitable only because of the unusually high yield of silver from the galena which averaged 30 ounces per ton. The three mines immediately to the west of Edmundbyers are all late ventures. The statistical returns indicate that Harehope Gill (NZ 009485) was worked between approximately 1852 and 1866, Burnhope (NZ 005489) between 1880 and 1887 and Swandale (NZ 004492) between about 1876 and 1887. However, according to the county historian, Surtees, the neighbouring smelt mill at Feldon was built much earlier, in the reign of Charles II. This was acquired by the London Lead Company in 1725 and was operated by the Quakers until 1806 when the leases of the mines within the Manor of Muggleswick were surrendered. In 1831 the mill was up for sale, but when it ceased work is uncertain. Today the ruined buildings, the flue chambers and several piles of black slag are visible.

The **Eudon Grove** (NY 982459) mine hidden in a secluded gill at the head of the valley is another old enterprise. On the first edition of the Ordnance Survey (1857) the site is marked as an old mine. Today the ruined mine shop and the adjacent level, the primitive washing floor and the isolation of the site recall the spirit of the eighteenth century adventurers.

Return to Hexham via the A68.

Glossary

Adit A tunnel driven to drain a mine.

Assay A test of the ores by chemical examination.

Bail or bale hill Ancient smelting place.

Bing Standard measurement of lead concentrate, equivalent to 8 hundredweight.

Bingstead Place where ore was tipped prior to smelting.

Black Jack Sphalerite, zinc sulphide, also known as blende.

Blende Zinc Ore

Bouse Unwashed ore straight from the mine.

Bouseteems Place where unwashed ore is placed prior to dressing.

Bucker A hammer for crushing bouse by hand on a knockstone.

Buddle A term referred [sic] to a wide range of apparatus for dressing fine ores named after John Buddle (1773-1843).

Bunning Timber staging placed between the walls of a vein to provide a working platform.

Colrake A rake similar to a garden rake used in buddling.

Concentrate Ore dressed ready for the smelter.

Crosscut Level driven through barren ground from one vein to another.

Cupola Old term for smelting furnace.

Deadwork Necessary work which only produces waste material or deads.

Dress To treat ore from the mine so that the waste is discarded and lead concentrate is produced for the smelter.

Fines Smallest material produced during dressing.

Flat A horizontal ore deposit.

Gad Steel wedge used to split rock.

Galena Lead sulphide.

Gangue Unmarketable minerals, the opposite to pay dirt.

Gin or whim gin Machinery, usually horse driven, for hoisting from the mine.

Groove An old term for a mine.

Horse level Main haulage level, sometimes known as galloway level.

Hotching Jigging as part of the process of dressing the ore.

Hush Man-made ravine caused by discharging a head of water from a reservoir to clear surface soil and expose or work a surface vein.

Incline (railway) Steep gradient usually operated by stationery haulage engines.

Jigs Machinery used on the dressing floor for separating out the lead.

Level Horizontal entrance into a mine.

Middlings Second quality ore only partly dressed.

Mine shop Lodging house at remote mines or more simply just a place where men could change from mine clothes.

Old man Former miners, old workings.

Opencut Opencast mining.

Plate Shale bed.

Rake Line of the vein at the surface.

Smiddum Smallest material produced during dressing.

Spoil heap Waste heap.

Stamps Crushing machine.

Stemples Crossbars of wood fixed in shaft for climbing.

Stope To work vertically up the vein.

Tailings Worthless material after dressing.

Tontale A contract for payment according to weight of lead smelted.

Trial Small working usually exploratory.

Trommel Revolving screen for sizing ore.

Twyer Blow pipe (see Ch. 4, p. 57)

Wallet Week's rations which the miners took to the mine shop.

Water blast A method of ventilation.

Whimsy shafts Haulage shafts into mine

Bibliography

Much of the source material for this booklet is not easily accessible to the general public; but the following books are – and Hunt's book contains an excellent bibliography.

1. Raistrick and Jennings, *A History of Lead Mining in the Pennines* is the standard general history which enables useful comparisons to be made with the other lead mining areas of Yorkshire and Derbyshire.

2. C J Hunt, *The Lead Miners of the Northern Pennines* is a social and economic history based largely upon the Blackett-Beaumont papers.

3. K C Dunham, *Geology of the Northern Pennine Orefield* is a detailed geological study of the area which includes some useful historical notes about individual mines.

4. Raistrick and Roberts, *Life and Work of the Northern Lead Miner* is copiously illustrated with photographs from the archives of Beamish Museum.

5. W R Mitchell, *Pennine Lead Miner: Eric Richardson of Nenthead.*